ENVIRONMENTAL EDUCATION

ENVIRONMENTAL EDUCATION

By

V. C. Pandey

ISHA

Environmental Education

ISBN : 978-81-820-5175-1

First Published 2008, reprint 2014 in India by
Isha Books
B-69, New Gupta Colony,
New DDA Market, New Delhi - 110009
Printed at : Sagar Color Scan, New Delhi.

Preface

One of the most formidable and ever more intractable challenges facing humans today is coexisting with the other living creatures on Earth. Meeting this challenge will require environmental education, both formal and informal.

Environmental education is a learning process that increases people's knowledge and awareness about the environment and associated challenges, develops the necessary skills and expertise to address these challenges, and fosters attitudes, motivations, and commitments to make informed decisions and take responsible action. It enhances critical thinking, problem solving, and effective decision-making skills and enables individuals to weigh various sides of an environmental issue to make informed and responsible decisions.

Teaching about the natural and built environment provides a real-world context for learning by linking the classroom to the students' community. Students are engaged in hands-on, active learning that increases their knowledge and awareness about the environment. Because environmental education encourages inquiry and investigation, students develop critical thinking, problem-solving, and effective decision-making skills. Environmentally literate students become citizens who are able to weigh various sides of an environmental issue and make responsible decisions as individuals and as members of their community. Quality, standards-based environmental education improves everyday life by protecting human health and encouraging stewardship of natural resources.

The past several decades have seen increasing awareness of the explosive growth in environmental problems throughout the world. A great majority of nations have, in fact, committed themselves through treaty obligations to providing environmental education. Environmental education has been expanding at all levels—primary, secondary, and tertiary. It is crucial to human well-being and survival that teachers at all levels throughout the world educate both themselves and their students to accept certain new ways of thinking.

Everyone who is responsible for educational policy or entrusted to carry it out should be made aware of the legally binding agreements entered into by their governments regarding environmental education; the current status of environmental education in both developed and developing countries; the authoritative encouragement and guidance offered by major environmental organizations and others; and the conceptual basis upon which all environmental education must rest if it is to achieve its purposes.

The nature, scope and importance of environmental education is described elaborately in this volume. It is designed to acquaint the readers with latest developments and researches in the field. It will serve as a highly beneficial reference tool for teachers, policy makers, students and environmental activists.

Editor

CONTENTS

1

Scope and Nature of Environmental Education

DEFINITION OF ENVIRONMENT

An environment is a complex of external factors that acts on a system and determines its course and form of existence. An environment may be thought of as a superset, of which the given system is a subset. An environment may have one or more parameters, physical or otherwise. The environment of a given system must necessarily interact with that system.

Generally, the environment or milieu of some object or action consists of the substances, circumstances, objects, or conditions by which it is surrounded or in which it occurs. Although the two terms are usually synonyms, some sciences prefer the less common milieu to avoid confusion with the more well-known meanings of environment in ecology, politics, and sociology.

In biology, environment may be defined as the complex of climatic, biotic, social and edaphic factors that acts upon an organism and determines its form and survival. It, therefore, includes everything that may directly affect the metabolism or behavior of a living organism or species, including light, air, water, soil, and other living beings.

UNDERSTANDING ECOLOGY

Ecology is the branch of science that studies the distribution and abundance of living organisms, and the interactions between organisms and their environment. The environment of an organism includes both its physical habitat, which can be described as the sum of local abiotic factors like climate and geology, as well as the other organisms which share its habitat. The term was coined in 1866 by the German biologist Ernst Haeckel from the Greek oikos meaning "household" and logos meaning "science:" the "study of the household of nature."

Ecological systems are studied at several different levels from individuals and populations to ecosystems and biosphere level. Ecology is a multi-disciplinary science, drawing on many other branches of science.

Applied ecology is the practice of employing ecological principles and understanding to solve real world problems. Examples include measuring the economic worth of ecosystems, calculating fishing quotas, measuring environmental impact from construction or logging, building a case for the conservation of a species, and determining the most effective way to protect a species.

In a broader sense, ecology is can also mean:

— the natural environment, or

— an analysis or study using the principles and methods of ecology.

For example, human ecology looks at humans and their interactions with the natural environment. Political ecology takes on both alternative meanings, and may use ecology's methods in a new context by looking at interactions of societies and states rather than species or populations, but may also mean politics related to environmental issues.

Ecology, as a scientific disipline, does not itself dictate what is right or wrong. However maintaining biodiversity within ecosystems and related ecological goals (such as preventing species extinctions) have become scientific ways to express the goals of environmentalism and has given scientific methodology, measure, and terminology to environmental issues, making the two heavily linked. A holistic view is also stressed in both ecology and environmentalism.

Scope

Ecology is usually considered a branch of biology, the general science that studies living beings. These can be studied at several levels, from proteins and nucleic acids (in biochemistry and molecular biology), cells (in cellular biology), organisms (in botanics, zoology, and other similar disciplines), and finally at the level of populations, communities, and ecosystems — which are the subjects of ecology. Conversely, some people consider ecology to be the parent discipline and biology to be the sub-disciple, since ecology includes not only the interactions between organsisms, but also their interactions with their surroundings.

Because of its focus on the broadest level of life and on the interrelations between living beings and their environment, ecology draws heavily on other branches of science, such as geology and geography, meteorology, pedology, chemistry, and physics. For this reason, ecology is often said to be a holistic science.

— the behavioural relationship between individuals of a species — for example, the study of the queen bee, and how it relates to the worker bees and the drones.

— the organized activity of a species — for example, the activity of the bee assures the pollination of flowering plants. A bee hive additionally produces honey which is consumed by other species, such as bears.

— and the environment of this activity — for example, the consequences of the environmental change on the bee activity.

Bees may die out due to environmental changes. The environment at the same time both affects and is a consequence of this activity and is thus intertwined with the survival of the species.

Disciplines of ecology

Ecology is a broad science that encompasses many specialized branches, including ecophysiology which studies the relations between a single type of organism and the factors of its environment; population ecology or autecology, , which studies the relations between a population of individuals of the same species and its environment; community ecology or synecology, which studies the relations between one's community, in addition to individuals of different species within his environment, often using the concept of ecological succession.

For modern ecologists, ecology can be studied at several levels: population level (individuals of the same species), biocenose level (or community of species), ecosystem level, and biosphere level.

The Earth, from an ecological point of view, consists of several compartments, the hydrosphere (or sphere of water), the lithosphere (or sphere of soils and rocks) and the atmosphere (or sphere of the air). The biosphere, sometimes described as fourth envelope, is the part of the planet on which the life developed. It is a very thin surface layer, which goes down to 11000 meters of depth to rising up to 15000 meters of altitude, although the majority of life live in the zone located between -100 meters and +100 meters.

Life first developed in the hydrosphere, at low depth, in the photic zone. Multicellular organisms then appeared and colonized benthic zones. Terrestrial life developed later, after the ozone layer protecting living beings from UV rays formed. Diversification of terrestrial species is thought to be increased by the continents drifting apart, or alternately, colliding. Biosphere and biodiversity are inseparable characteristics of the

Earth. Biosphere is defined as being the sphere of life, whereas biodiversity is its diversity. The sphere is the container, whereas diversity is the contents. This diversity is expressed at the same time at the ecological level (ecosystem), population level (intraspecific diversity) and species level (specific diversity).

The biosphere contains great quantities of elements such as carbon, nitrogen and oxygen. Other elements, such as phosphorus, calcium, and potassium, are also essential to life. At the ecosystem and biosphere level, there is a permanent recycling of all these elements, which alternate between the mineral state and the organic state.

While there is a slight input of geothermal energy, the bulk of the functioning of the ecosystem is primarily based on the input of solar energy. Plants convert light into chemical energy by the process of photosynthesis, which creates glucose (a simple sugar) and releases free oxygen. Glucose thus becomes the secondary energy source which drives the ecosystem. Some of this glucose is used directly by other organisms for energy. Other sugar molecules can be converted to other molecules such as amino acids. Plants use some of this sugar, concentrated in nectar to entice pollinators to aid them in reproduction. (Honeybees concentrate the sugar still further as honey, which can be said to be "stored summer sunshine").

Cellular respiration is the process by which organisms (like mammals) breakdown the glucose back to its constituents, water and carbon dioxide, gaining back the stored energy the sun originally gave to the plants. The proportion of photosynthetic activity of plants to the respiration of other organisms determines the specific composition of the Earth's atmosphere, particularly its oxygen level. Global air currents mix the atmosphere and maintain nearly the same balance in areas of intense biological activity and areas of slight biological activity.

Water is also exchanged between the hydrosphere, the lithosphere, the atmosphere and the biosphere in regular cycles.

The oceans are large tanks, which store water, ensure a thermal and climatic stability, as well as the transport of the chemical elements thanks to large oceanic currents. For better understanding of how the biosphere works, and the dysfunctions related to human activity, American scientists carried out, under greenhouses, a small-scale model of the biosphere, called Biosphere II.

Concept of an ecosystem

The first principle of ecology is that each living organism has an ongoing and continual relationship with every other element that makes up its environment. An ecosystem can be defined as any situation where there is interaction between organisms and their environment.

The ecosystem is composed of two entities, the entirety of life (called the biocenose) and the medium that life exists in (the biotope). Within the ecosystem, species are connected and dependent upon one another in the food chain, and exchange energy and matter between themselves and with their environment.

The concept of an ecosystem can apply to units of variable size, such as a pond, a field, or a piece of deadwood. A unit of smaller size is called a microecosystem. For example, an ecosystem can be a stone and all the life under it. A mesoecosystem could be a forest, and a macroecosystem a whole ecoregion, with its watershed.

Ecosystems are often classified by reference to the biotopes concerned. The following ecosystems may be defined :

— as continental ecosystems (or terrestrial), such as forest ecosystems, meadow ecosystems (meadows, steppes, savannas), or agro-ecosystems (agricultural systems).

— as ecosystems of inland waters, such as lentic ecosystems (lakes, ponds) or lotic ecosystems (rivers)

— as oceanic ecosystems (seas, oceans).

Another classification can be done by reference to its communities (for example a human ecosystem).

In ecology, an ecosystem is a community of organisms (plant, animal and other living organisms - also referred as biocenose) together with their environment (or biotope), functioning as a unit.

The term ecosystem first appeared in a 1935 publication by the British ecologist Arthur Tansley. However, the term had been coined already in 1930 by Tansley's colleague Roy Clapham, who was asked if he could think of a suitable word to denote the physical and biological components of an environment considered in relation to each other as a unit.

An ecosystem is a dynamic and complex whole, interacting as an ecological unit. Some consider it is a basic unit in ecology, only a structured functional unit in equilibrium, characterized by energy and matter flows between the different elements that compose it. But others consider this vision or a self-standing unit with coherent and stable flows only to be a bit restrictive.

An ecosystem may be of very different size. It may be a whole forest, as well as a small pond. Different ecosystems are often separated by geographical barriers, like deserts, mountains or oceans, or are isolated otherwise, like lakes or rivers. As these borders are never rigid, ecosystems tend to blend into each other. As a result, the whole earth can be seen as a single ecosystem, or a lake can be divided into several ecosystems, depending on the used scale.

The organisms in an ecosystem are usually well balanced with each other and with their environment. Introduction of new environmental factors or new species can have disastrous results, eventually leading to the collapse of an ecosystem and the death of many of its native species. The abstract notion of ecological health attempts to measure the robustness and capacity for recovery of a natural ecosystem.

Ecosystem and ecoregion terms are often confused (large ecosystems being called ecoregions), but there is a large consensus to define ecoregions as being geographical defined units, relatively large, land or water, with distinctive features. Ecoregions are a way to codify the different regions within which are observed particular patterns or similarities in ecosystems.

Dynamics and stability

The biotope is a region environmentally uniform, characterized by a whole set of geological, geographical and climatological parameters, which are called abiotic ecological factors:

- water, is at the same time, an essential element to life, as well as a milieu
- air, which provides oxygen and carbon dioxide to living species, and allows the dissemination of pollen and spores
- soil, at the same time source of nutriment and support of development
- temperature, which should not exceed certain extremes, even if tolerance to heat is significant for some species
- light, allowing photosynthesis.

Biocenose, or community, is a group of populations of plants, animals, micro-organisms. Each population is the result of procreations between individuals of same species and cohabiting in a given place and at a given time. When a population consists of an insufficient number of individuals, the species is threatened with extinction, either by underpopulation, or by because of consanguinity. A population can be reduced for several reasons, for example, disappearance of its habitat (destruction of a forest) or by excessive predation (such as the hunting of a given species).

Biocenose is characterized by biotic ecological factors of two types: intraspecific and interspecific relations.

Intraspecific relations are those which are established between individuals of the same species, forming a population. They are relations of co-operation or competition, with division of the territory, and sometimes organization in hierarchical societies.

Interspecific relations, i.e. those existing between different species, are numerous, and usually described according to their beneficial, detrimental or neutral effect (for example, symbiosis (relation ++) or competition (relation —)). The most significant relation is the relation of predation (to eat or to be eaten), which leads to the essential concepts in ecology of food chains (for example, the grass is consumed by the herbivore, itself consumed by a carnivore, itself consumed by a carnivore of larger size). Ecological niche is the area shared by two species when they live at the same place with the same type of diet.

The existing interactions between the various living beings go along with a permanent mixing of mineral and organic substances, absorbed by organisms for their growth, their maintenance and their reproduction, to be finally rejected as waste. These permanent recyclings of the elements (in particular carbon, oxygen and nitrogen) as well as the water are called biogeochemical cycles. They guarantee a durable stability of the biosphere (at least when human influence and extreme weather phenomena are left aside). This self-regulation, supported by negative feedback controls, ensures the perenniality of the ecosystems. It is shown by the very stable concentrations of most elements of each compartment. This is referred to as homeostasis. The ecosystem also tends to evolve to a state of ideal balance, reached after a succession of events, the climax (for example a pond can become a peat bog).

Spatial relationships and subdivisions of land

Ecosystems are not isolated from each other, but are interrelated. For example, water may circulate between ecosystems by the means of a river or ocean current. Water itself, as a liquid medium, even defines ecosystems. Some species, such as salmon or freshwater eels move between marine systems and fresh-water systems. These relationships between the ecosystems lead to the concept of a biome.

A biome is a homogeneous ecological formation that exists over a vast region, such as tundra or steppes. The biosphere comprises all of the Earth's biomes — the entirety of places where life is possible — from the highest mountains to the depths of the oceans.

Biomes correspond rather well to subdivisions distributed along the latitudes, from the equator towards the poles, with differences based on to the physical environment (for example, oceans or mountain ranges) and to the climate. Their variation is generally related to the distribution of species according to their ability to tolerate temperature and/or dryness. For example, one may find photosynthetic algae only in the photic part of the ocean (where light penetrates), while conifers are mostly found in mountains.

Though this is a simplification of more complicated scheme, latitude and altitude approximate a good representation of the distribution of biodiversity within the biosphere. Very generally, the richness of biodiversity (as well for animal than plant species) is decreasing most rapidly near the equator (as in Brazil) and less rapidly as one approaches the poles. The biosphere may also be divided into ecozone, which are very well defined today and primarily follow the continental borders. The ecozones are themselves divided into ecoregions, though there is not agreement on their limits.

Ecosystem productivity

In an ecosystem, the connections between species are generally related to food and their role in the food chain. There are three categories of organisms:

— *producers* — plants which are capable of photosynthesis

— *consumers* — animals, which can be primary consumers (herbivorous), or secondary or tertiary consumers (carnivorous).

— *decomposers* — bacteria, mushrooms which degrade organic matter of all categories, and restore minerals to the environment.

These relations form sequences, in which each individual consumes the preceding one and is consumed by the one following, in what are called food chains or food network. In a food network, there will be fewer organisms at each level as one follows the links of the network up the chain. These concepts lead to the idea of biomass (the total living matter in a given place), of primary productivity (the increase in the mass of plants during a given time) and of secondary productivity (the living matter produced by consumers and the decomposers in a given time).

These two last ideas are key, since they make it possible to evaluate the load capacity — the number of organisms which can be supported by a given ecosystem. In any food network, the energy contained in the level of the producers is not completely transferred to the consumers. Thus, from an energy point of view, it is more efficient for humans to be primary consumers (to get nourishment from grains and vegetables) than as secondary consumers (from herbivores such as beef and veal), and more still than as a tertiary consumer (from eating carnivores).

The productivity of ecosystems is sometimes estimated by comparing three types of land-based ecosystems and the total of aquatic ecosystems:

— the forests (1/3 of the Earth's land area) contain dense biomasses and are very productive. The total production of the world's forests corresponds to half of the primary production.

— savannas, meadows, and marshes (1/3 of the Earth's land area) contain less dense biomasses, but are productive.

These ecosystems represent the major part of what humans depend on for food.

— extreme ecosystems in the areas with more extreme climates — deserts and semi-deserts, tundra, alpine meadows, and steppes — (1/3 of the Earth's surface) have very sparse biomasses and low productivity

— finally, the marine and fresh water ecosystems (3/4 of Earth's surface) contain very sparse biomasses (apart from the coastal zones).

Humanity's actions over the last few centuries have seriously reduced the amount of the Earth covered by forests (deforestation), and have increased agro-ecosystems (agriculture). In recent decades, an increase in the areas occupied by extreme ecosystems has occurred (desertification).

Ecological crisis

Generally, an ecological crisis is what occurs when the environment of life of a species or a population evolves in an unfavourable way to its survival. It may be that the environment quality degrades compared to the species needs, after a change of abiotic ecological factor (for example, an increase of temperature, less significant rainfalls).

It may be that the environment becomes unfavourable for the survival of a species (or a population) due to an increase pressure of predation (for example overfishing).

Lastly, it may be that the situation becomes unfavourable to the quality of life of the species (or the population) due to rise in the number of individuals (overpopulation).

Ecological crises may be more or less brutal (occurring between a few months to a few million years). They can also be of natural or anthropic origin. They may relate to one unique species or on the contrary, to a high number of species.

Lastly, an ecological crisis may be local (as an oil spill) or global (a rise in the sea level related to global warming).

According to its degree of endemism, a local crisis will have more or less significant consequences, from the death of many individuals to the total extinction of a species. Whatever its origin, disappearance of one or several species often will involve a rupture in the food chain, further impacting the survival of other species.

In the case of a global crisis, the consequences can be much more significant; some extinction events showed the disappearance of more than 90% of existing species at that time. However, it should be noted that the disappearance of certain species, such as the dinosaurs, by freeing an ecological niche, allowed the development and the diversification of the mammals. An ecological crisis thus paradoxically favored biodiversity.

Sometimes, an ecological crisis can be a specific and reversible phenomenon at the ecosystem scale. But more generally, the crises impact will last. Indeed, it rather is a connected series of events, that occur till a final point. From this stage, no return to the previous stable state is possible, and a new stable state will be set up gradually.

Lastly, if an ecological crisis can cause extinction, it can also more simply reduce the quality of life of the remaining individuals. Thus, even if the diversity of the human population is sometimes considered threatened, few people envision human disappearance at short span. However, epidemic diseases, famines, impact on health of reduction of air quality, food crises, reduction of living space, accumulation of toxic or non degradable wastes, threats on keystone species (great apes, panda, whales) are also factors influencing the well-being of people.

During the past decades, this increasing responsibility of humanity in some ecological crises has been clearly observed. Due to the increases in technology and a rapidly increasing population, humans have more influence on their own environment than any other ecosystem engineer.

Some usually quoted examples as ecological crises are

— Permian-Triassic extinction event 250 million of years ago

— Cretaceous-Tertiary extinction event 65 million years ago

— global warming related to the greenhouse effect. Warming could involve flooding of the Asian deltas, multiplication of extreme weather phenomena and changes in the nature and quantity of the food resources.

— Ozone layer hole issue

— Deforestation and desertification, with disappearance of many species.

— The nuclear meltdown at Chernobyl in 1986 caused the death of many people and animals from cancer, and caused mutations in a large number of animals and people. The area around the plant is now abandoned because of the large amount of radiation generated by the meltdown.

History of ecology

One of the first ecologists may have been Aristotle who had interest in many species of animals. He was followed by numerous naturalists such as Buffon and Carolus Linnaeus, whose work is usually considered the origin of modern ecology.

The botanical geography and Alexander von Humboldt

Throughout the 18th and the beginning of the 19th century, the great maritime powers such as Britain, Spain, and Portugal launched many world exploratory expeditions to develop maritime commerce with other countries, and to discover new natural resources, as well as to catalog them. At the beginning of the 18th century, about twenty thousand plant species were known, versus forty thousand at the beginning of the 19th century, and almost 400,000 today. These expeditions were joined by many scientists, including botanists, such as the German explorer Alexander von Humboldt. Humboldt is often considered the true father of ecology. He was the first to take on the study of the relationship between organisms and their environment. He exposed the existing relationships between observed plant species and climate, and described vegetation zones using latitude and altitude, a discipline now known as geobotany.

In 1804, for example, he reported an impressive number of species, particularly plants, for which he sought to explain their geographic distribution with respect to geological data. One of Humboldt's famous works was "Idea for a Plant Geography" (1805).

The notion of biocenose: Charles Darwin and Alfred Wallace

Towards 1850 there was a breakthrough in the field with the publishing of the work of Charles Darwin on The Origin of Species: Ecology passed from a repetitive, mechanical model to a biological, organic, and hence evolutionary model. Alfred Russel Wallace, contemporary and competitor to Darwin, was first to propose a "geography" of animal species. Several authors recognized at the time that species were not independent of each other, and grouped them into plant species, animal species, and later into communities of living beings or biocenose. This term was coined in 1877 by Karl Möbius.

The biosphere - Eduard Suess and Vladimir Vernadsky

By the 19th century, ecology blossomed due to new discoveries in chemistry by Lavoisier and de Saussure, notably the nitrogen cycle. After observing the fact that life developed only within strict limits of each compartment that makes up the atmosphere, hydrosphere, and lithosphere, the Austrian geologist Eduard Suess proposed the term biosphere in 1875. Suess proposed the name biosphere for the conditions promoting life, such as those found on Earth, which includes flora, fauna, minerals, matter cycles, et cetera.

In the 1920s Vladimir I. Vernadsky, a Russian geologist who had defected to France, detailed the idea of the biosphere in his work "The biosphere", and described the fundamental principles of the biogeochemical cycles. He thus redefined the biosphere as the sum of all ecosystems.

First ecological damages were reported in the 18th century, as the multiplication of colonies caused deforestation. Since the 19th century, with the industrial revolution, more and more pressing concerns have grown about the impact of human activity on the environment. The term ecologist has been in use since the end of the 19th century.

The ecosystem: Arthur Tansley

Over the 19th century, botanical geography and zoogeography combined to form the basis of biogeography. This science, which deals with habitats of species, seeks to explain the reasons for the presence of certain species in a given location. It was in 1935 that Arthur Tansley, the British ecologist, coined the term ecosystem, the interactive system established between the biocenose (the group of living creatures), and their biotope, the environment in which they live. Ecology thus became the science of ecosystems.

Tansley's concept of the ecosystem was adopted by the energetic and influential biology educator Eugene Odum. Along with his brother, Howard Odum, Eugene P. Odum wrote a textbook which educated more than one generation of biologists and ecologists in North America.

Human ecology

Human ecology began in the 1920s, through the study of changes in vegetation succession in the city of Chicago. It became a distinct field of study in the 1970s. This marked the first recognition that humans, who had colonized all of the Earth's continents, were a major ecological factor. Humans greatly modify the environment through the development of the habitat, by intensive exploitation activities such as logging and fishing, and as side effects of agriculture, mining, and industry. Besides ecology and biology, this discipline involved many other natural and social sciences, such as anthropology and ethnology, economics, demography, architecture and urban planning, medicine and psychology, and many more. The development of human ecology led to the increasing role of ecological science in the design and management of cities.

James Lovelock and the Gaia hypothesis

The Gaia theory, proposed by James Lovelock, in his work Gaia: A New Look at Life on Earth, advanced the view that the Earth should be regarded as a single living macro-organism. In particular, it argued that the ensemble of living organisms has jointly evolved an ability to control the global environment — by influencing major physical parameters as the composition of the atmosphere, the evaporation rate, the chemistry of soils and oceans — so as to maintain conditions favorable to life.

This vision was largely a sign of the times, in particular the growing perception after the Second World War that human activities such as nuclear energy, industrialization, pollution, and overexploitation of natural resources, fueled by exponential population growth, were threatening to create catastrophes on a planetary scale. Thus Lovelock's Gaia hypothesis, while controversial among scientists, was embraced by many environmental movements as an inspiring view: their Earth-mother, Gaia, was "becoming sick from humans and their activities".

Conservation and environmental movements

Indeed, since the 19th century, ecology has been obviously relevant to social and philosophical movements related to protection of the natural environment, such as conservationism and environmentalism. Today ecology is a major political topic, and a source of ideology for major political organizations such as the Green Party and Greenpeace.

Ecology and global policy

Ecology became a central part of the World's politics as early as 1971, UNESCO launched a research program called Man and Biosphere, with the objective of increasing knowledge about the mutual relationship between humans and nature. A few years later it defined the concept of Biosphere Reserve.

In 1972, the United Nations held the first international conference on the human environment in Stockholm, prepared by René Dubos and other experts. This conference was the origin of the phrase "Think Globally, Act Locally". The next major events in ecology were the development of the concept of biosphere and the appearance of terms "biological diversity" — or now more commonly biodiversity — in the 1980s. These terms were developed during the Earth Summit in Rio de Janeiro in 1992, where the concept of the biosphere was recognized by the major international organizations, and risks associated with reductions in biodiversity were publicly acknowledged.

Then, in 1997, the dangers the biosphere was facing were recognized from an international point of view at the conference leading to the Kyoto Protocol. In particular, this conference highlighted the increasing dangers of the greenhouse effect — related to the increasing concentration of greenhouse gases in the atmosphere, leading to global changes in climate. In Kyoto, most of the world's nations recognized the importance of looking at ecology from a global point of view, on a worldwide scale, and to take into account the impact of humans on the Earth's environment.

ENVIRONMENTAL EDUCATION

Definition

Teaching about the natural and built environment provides a real-world context for learning by linking the classroom to the students' community. Students are engaged in hands-on, active learning that increases their knowledge and awareness about the environment. Because environmental education encourages inquiry and investigation, students develop critical thinking, problem-solving, and effective decision-making skills. Environmentally literate students become citizens who are able to weigh various sides of an environmental issue and make responsible decisions as individuals and as members of their community. Quality, standards-based environmental education improves everyday life by protecting human health and encouraging stewardship of natural resources.

Importance of environmental education

One of the most formidable and ever more intractable challenges facing humans today is coexisting with the other living creatures on Earth. Meeting this challenge will require appropriate education, both formal and informal. Everyone who is responsible for educational policy or entrusted to carry it out should be made aware of the legally binding agreements entered into by their governments regarding environmental education; the current status of environmental education in both developed and developing countries; the authoritative encouragement and guidance offered by major environmental organizations and others; and the conceptual basis upon which all environmental education must rest if it is to achieve its purposes.

A great majority of nations have, in fact, committed themselves through treaty obligations to providing environmental education. It thus becomes germane that "every treaty in force is binding upon the parties to it and must be performed by them in good faith." Indeed, several countries—such as Costa Rica, Germany, and the United States—have enshrined this basic principle of pacta sunt servanda in their national constitutions. Three important multilateral treaties, in particular, commit their parties to providing environmental education to their citizenry:

— The approximately 131 countries (not, as yet, including the United States) that are parties to the Convention on the Rights of the Child (which came into force on 20 September 1990) have agreed that "the education of the child shall be directed to . . .the development of respect for the natural environment."

— About 126 countries (including the United States) are parties to the Convention Concerning the Protection of the World Cultural and Natural Heritage (which came into force on 17 December 1975) and have agreed to "endeavour by all appropriate means, and in particular by educational and information programmes, to strengthen appreciation and respect by their peoples of the . . . natural heritage defined [as] natural features consisting of physical and biological formations or groups of such formations, which are of outstanding universal value from the aesthetic or scientific point of view; geological and physiographical formations and precisely delineated areas which constitute the habitat of threatened species of animals and plants of outstanding universal value from the point of view of science or conservation; natural sites or precisely delineated natural areas of outstanding universal value from the point of view of science, conservation or natural beauty."

— The approximately 112 countries (not including the United States) that are parties to Protocol I of 1977 on the Protection of Victims of International Armed Conflicts (which came into force on 7 December 1978) have agreed that "it is prohibited to employ methods or means of warfare which are intended, or may be expected, to cause widespread, long-term and severe damage to the natural environment" and that "care shall be taken in warfare to protect the natural environment against widespread, long-term and severe damage, [this protection including] a prohibition of the use of methods or means of warfare which are intended or may be expected to cause such damage to the natural environment and thereby to prejudice the health or survival of the population." In addition, "the High Contracting Parties undertake, in time of peace as in time of armed conflict, to disseminate . . . this Protocol as widely as possible in their respective countries and, in particular, to include the study thereof in their programmes of military instruction and to encourage the study thereof by the civilian population, so that [this Protocol] may become known to the armed forces and to the civilian population."

— Each country not yet party to these three multilateral treaties should accede to them so that the benefits to both humankind and nature can more readily become universal. Environmental education is clearly necessary to develop the public conscience that is appropriate to the cultural and legal norms that are outlined in these treaties.

The past several decades have seen increasing awareness of the explosive growth in environmental problems throughout the world. One indicator of this awareness has been the proliferation of new journals devoted to environment and conservation. For example, at least six journals aimed specifically at teachers of environmental studies now exist: Journal of Environmental Education, begun in 1969 in Washington, D.C.; Environmental Education Report & Newsletter, begun in 1973 in Hanover, New Hampshire; Connect, begun in 1976 in Paris; Development Education, begun in 1980 in Lancashire, England; Conservation Education, begun in 1981 in Guildford, England; and Environmental Education, Information, begun in 1981 in Manchester, England.

Environmental education has been similarly expanding at all levels—primary, secondary, and tertiary (higher and specialized)—at least within the developed countries of the world. In the United States, for example, the National

Environmental Education Act provides for substantial support for environmental education in local primary and secondary school systems. At the tertiary level, environmental offerings at undergraduate schools and at some professional schools have expanded enormously. However, graduate environmental programs are said to be faltering a bit for lack of sufficient federal funding.

The status of environmental education outside the developed countries is far lower than desirable. Relatively little formal environmental education has permeated developing countries, despite considerable efforts in recent decades by the United Nations Educational, Scientific & Cultural Organization, the United Nations Environment Programme (UNEP), and the World Conservation Union (IUCN). This is not surprising, considering that economic conditions in many developing countries are not only dismal but also worsening year by year (for example, gross national product per capita has been declining continually for many years in 90 or more developing countries). With the overall educational infrastructure grossly inadequate in much of the Third World, resources to institute appropriate environmental education are, for the most part, simply not available, even when this education is recognized as a desirable innovation.

All of the principal recent blueprints for coping with the world's pervasive environmental predicament have stressed the value of environmental education. The World Commission on Environment and Development has urged that "environmental education should be included in and should run throughout the other disciplines of the formal education curriculum at all levels—to foster a sense of responsibility for the state of the environment and to teach students how to monitor, protect, and improve it."

IUCN, in partnership with UNEP and the World Wide Fund for Nature, has stressed that "governments, through central and local education authorities, should review the present state of environmental education (including social education) and should make it a part of all courses at primary and secondary, and many at tertiary level. The World Resources Institute, together with IUCN and UNEP, has insisted that "at the national level, ecological literacy belongs alongside other basic skills. National curricula on biodiversity . . . should emphasize biodiversity's contributions to community health and welfare, as well as to ecosystems, and should tie ecological, economic, and social themes together."

The United Nations Conference on Environment and Development agreed, writing that "education is critical for achieving environmental and ethical awareness, values and attitudes, skills and behaviour consistent with sustainable development and for effective public participation in decision-making." And a distinguished group of 22 university presidents from 13 developed and developing countries recently pledged to have their institutions play educational leadership roles in the necessary quest for a sustainable future.

Little doubt can remain that public opinion against environmental abuse—and, presumably, in time, cultural norms concerning the environment—must be reinforced at every level of education. Traditional approaches to education, however, do not appear to be ready to meet the challenge. Despite this situation, insufficient attention is being paid to the development of the methodology of environmental education. To begin with, it is essential that a holistic (global) and long-term sustainable) viewpoint be fostered. Indeed, to establish lasting pro-environmental, frugal, nonmilitaristic, and egalitarian norms, it may well be necessary for many, if not most, schools to restructure their curricula so as to de-emphasize the anthropocentric, competitive, hierarchical, and unquestioning attitudes so prevalent today.

In the search for the social sanity that would permit sustainable and equitable development in harmony with nature, humans must first accept the conclusion that abuse of the environment is largely a product of misguided anthropocentrism and ignorance. Humans must also accept the notion that the cultural norms that underlie the prevailing anti-environmental attitudes are not immutable but can, in fact, be changed, inter alia, through such societal institutions as schools.

It is crucial to human well-being and survival that teachers at all levels throughout the world educate both themselves and their students to accept certain new ways of thinking. These new cultural norms must incorporate a recognition of at least the following eight concepts:

- the potentially cataclysmic threat to both human civilization and the natural world posed by nuclear and other weapons of mass destruction;
- the overall incompatibility of militarism and environmentalism;
- the widespread incongruence between political and ecological borders and, thus, the need for international cooperation in dealing with many environmental problems;
- the necessity of disposing solid, liquid, and gaseous wastes on a basis of sustained discard;
- the necessity of managing renewable natural resources on a basis of sustained yield;
- the necessity that any development or use of natural resources must be not only sustainable but also equitable;
- the importance of thinking in terms of future generations; and, perhaps above all,
- the rights of the other living things with which humans share the Earth.

Ultimately, formal education must establish unequivocally the concept that all human actions are to be judged not only by traditional ethical standards but also by ecological ones. In short, teachers must be able to develop within themselves and in their students a true sense both of human dignity and of humanity's place in nature.

It is thus a tragedy that the great majority of nations devote far too little to their educational sectors. Despite the relatively widespread annual increases in allocations to education within developing countries, populations have been growing so fast that per-capita education spending has not risen in more than a decade. Nonetheless, it remains incumbent upon educators everywhere to revise their curricula as needed to conform to the legal and ethical necessity of providing appropriate environmental education at all levels.

At least two avenues are open to most developing countries to strengthen their educational sector, both of which should be vigorously pursued: the institution of population controls and the reallocation of funds to the educational sector from military expenditures beyond those necessary to maintain a nonprovocative deterrent or defensive armed force. Moreover, it seems to be in the enlightened self-interest of the developed world to support efforts aimed at achieving universal primary and secondary education and more widespread tertiary education. Here, too, the source of funding most readily available is from a comparable reallocation of military expenditures—which, in developed countries, currently amount to some $2 billion per day.

Guiding principles of Environmental Education

Environmental education is a learning process that increases people's knowledge and awareness about the environment and associated challenges, develops the necessary skills and expertise to address these challenges, and fosters attitudes, motivations, and commitments to make informed decisions and take responsible action. Environmental education enhances critical thinking, problem solving, and effective decision-making skills and enables individuals to weigh various sides of an environmental issue to make informed and responsible decisions.

To help clarify the relationship between knowledge, skills, and action, educators have developed a framework and set of goal levels that stress a hierarchical approach to environmental literacy.

Goal levels

— *Ecological concepts:* Provides knowledge to make ecologically sound environmental decisions

— *Conceptual awareness:* Develops awareness of how individual and collective behaviors influence the quality of life and the quality of the environment

— *Issue investigation and evaluation:* Develops the knowledge and skills to investigate environmental issues and evaluate solutions for remediating them

— *Environmental action skills:* Develops skills for taking positive actions to help resolve environmental issues

Research findings indicate that in order for individuals and groups to make informed decisions and take responsible actions regarding the environment, they need to be thoroughly exposed to all four goal levels-not just the first two. Findings also indicate that the quality of environmental actions tends to improve when people have learned and used issue analysis and investigation skills.

Need and relevance to everyday lives

All members of society depend on natural resources to survive. The availability of these resources has limits. It is essential, therefore, that the public understand the importance of the environment to their quality of life and that they have the knowledge, tools, and ethic to live in ways that minimize the impact of their actions on the environment. In short, to live sustainably. Environmental education provides the public with the knowledge, tools, and ethic to enable them to make informed and responsible decisions to live sustainably.

The public is concerned about environmental quality. Several public opinion polls conducted in the past five years demonstrate that the citizens are worried about air and water quality, support an expanded givernment's role in environmental protection, and are concerned about the links between health and environment. For example, in US, in a 1994 public opinion poll conducted for the National Wildlife Federation indicated that despite concern about crime, the economy, and health care, voters do not want to roll back environmental protection and are especially concerned about clean water, pesticide contamination, and other issues related to human health and the environment. More than 40 percent of those polled felt that current laws and regulations do not go far enough in protecting the environment, which supports earlier surveys that found that environmental concerns are "urgent" and need to be addressed. The environment also is consistently ranked by young people as "one of the most important" issues facing the planet.

Public's ability to respond

Although much of the survey data demonstrates public concern about the environment, concern by itself does not necessarily indicate that individuals are taking appropriate actions to ensure environmental protection. for example, results of a 1991 poll released by The Wall Street Journal showed that 80 percent of Americans call themselves environmentalists, yet in that same poll, nearly 55 percent could not recall a single instance during the past six months when they bought one product instead of another for environmental concerns.

The actual level of public understanding about the basic scientific concepts that explain and offer solutions to environmental threats such as those posed by global change and wetlands destruction remains limited. Without sufficient knowledge and training, the public may wish to respond to an environmental challenge, but may not be able to do so effectively because they lack sufficient scientific understanding of the problem.

Environmental education and training can help bridge the gap between the public's heightened awareness of and interest in protecting the environment and their need to become more knowledgeable about the scientific concepts that will enable them to more effectively respond to their concerns.

Demand for environmental education

Recent surveys indicate that there is solid support at local and state levels from educators, parents, and students. In a 1993 survey of science and social studies educators and nonformal educators working in zoos, museums, nature centers, and aquariums, more than 90 percent of the more than 2,000 educators who responded indicated that environmental education should be a priority in schools and nonformal institutions. In that same survey, educators indicated a need for more materials, training, and institutional commitment for environmental education.

Many state and national organizations and state and government's agencies also have been inundated with requests for environmental education materials, training, and support. For example, during the past five years, EPA's Environmental Education Division received approximately 10,000 grant proposals requesting approximately $300 million. During this period, Congress appropriated approximately $13 million for this program allowing EPA to support only approximately 1,200 projects. As another example, through a grant from EPA, the University of Michigan established and maintains an electronic system, called "EE-Link," designed to increase the ability of educators and other users to gain access to the wealth of environmental education information and materials that exist in various databases linked through the Internet. The University of Michigan reports that since "EE-Link" was established in 1993, public interest and access to Internet accessible databases and materials through "EE-Link" has grown considerably. By June 1996, for example, the University of Michigan reported receiving approximately 640,000 "hits" over a three month period on

"EE-Link" showing the significant interest for this type of information.

In nonformal surveys, local and state institutions indicate that they do not have the staff or resources to respond to increasing requests for environmental education materials and training.

Environmental education is relevant to our everyday lives because it can ensure the health and welfare of our nation by:

— protecting human health
— advancing quality education
— expanding employment opportunities
— promoting sustainable development
— protecting natural heritage

Protecting human health

The link between environmental challenges and human health is a major cause for public concern about the environment. Lead poisoning in paint and pipes, air pollution, pesticides in water and food supplies, increased threats of skin cancer from depletion of the ozone layer, and related environmental challenges are of growing concern to an increasing number of people. The public is especially concerned about the effects of these problems on their children and future generations. Environmental education helps prevent or mitigate environmental human health problems by providing the public with information on how individual and collective actions lead to environmental pollution, how pollutants may affect one's health, how to assess real versus exaggerated environmental health risks, and how to make informed and responsible decisions that prevent or mitigate the effects of pollution on one's health.

Advancing quality education

Educators and public officials generally believe that significant improvements are needed in the nation's public education system to enhance student learning. Many educational scholars and practitioners agree that ". . . our students are not doing well at thinking, reasoning, analyzing, predicting, estimating, or problem solving . . .". Many goals of the education reform movement emphasize the importance of strengthening core subjects such as math, science, and geography as well as teaching in an interdisciplinary manner across subject areas.

Education reformers are also looking for ways to improve student learning through greater use and development of critical-thinking and problem-solving skills. Finally, many reformers emphasize the importance of relating learning in the classroom to the needs and issues of the community.

Environmental education has tremendous potential for contributing to the goals of the education reform movement. For example, environmental education provides an opportunity to strengthen teaching in many core subjects, especially science, because it is the basis for solving many of our environmental challenges. Environmental education also provides an opportunity to strengthen interdisciplinary teaching because environmental topics can be addressed from many different perspectives, including scientific, historical, cultural, and political perspectives. Finally, environmental education can provide an important opportunity for teachers to bring actual local environmental challenges into the classroom for discussion and problem-solving. Infusing environmental education into all subject areas can lead to overall improvements in the educational system, including improvements in teaching the core subjects."

Expanding employment opportunities

Protecting the environment has the added value of creating new jobs for People. Employment opportunities cover the spectrum of careers, from manual labor to high technology and management. For example, there is an increasing demand for individuals with specialized scientific and technical skills to develop more effective environmental pollution prevention and control technologies. There is also a growing demand for trained workers in environmentally related fields. Projected revenues show consistent growth for environmental industries such as air pollution control, environmental energy sources, hazardous waste management, resource recovery, and instrument manufacturing.

The Environmental Business Journal reports a composite annual growth rate of 6 percent for these industries. This growth is also reflected in employment forecasts into the next century. Environmental education and training can help ensure an adequate supply of well-trained environmental personnel to deal with the nation's increasingly complex environmental challenges. Environmental education also improves the quality of the general work force.

Environmental education's emphasis on critical thinking and problem-solving better equips students to deal with rapidly changing technologies in the workplace. And environmental education opens new opportunities as the India exports its environmental skills and technologies to other nations.

Promoting sustainable development

The future health and welfare of our nation depends on our ability to use the Earth's resources sustainably. The United Nations World Commission on Environment and Development defines sustainable development as "development that meets the needs of the present without compromising the ability of future generations to meet their own needs." It is critical that we provide future generations of India with the same abilities and opportunities that current and past generations have had. In 1992, international leaders came together in Rio de Janeiro to participate in the United Nations Conference on Environment and Development. The product of UNCED, Agenda 21, provides guidance to countries so they can meet their own environmental and development goals.

Sustainable development poses two fundamental education challenges: one is to promote positive attitudes and informed decisions of citizens and government leaders that are conducive to sustainability. The other is to teach people at all levels the benefits of integrating conservation priorities with the need for development.

Environmental education has the potential to make a major contribution to sustainable development by demonstrating ways to overcome these two challenges.

First, environmental education research has identified key strategies for developing education programs that lead to responsible decision-making and action.

Second, environmental education practitioners have developed program models for incorporating a range of perspectives into the resolution of issues.

These tools and strategies, developed over decades by environmental educators and field tested on a range of issues where conflicts exist between different interest groups, can be applied immediately to sustainable development.

Protecting natural heritage

Interest in protecting India's natural heritage arises from the respect that most Indians hold for the nation's past and a belief in its future. It also stems from a desire to protect our natural areas and scenic landscapes, to enjoy them, and to pass them on to our children. India's natural heritage also includes the multitude of plant and animal species that inhabit our country. State and privately funded efforts to protect and manage species and their habitats reflect Indians' love for wildlife. Yet many citizens do not understand the ecological and economic importance of preserving biological diversity and that species can be strong indicators of the health of the environment.

Environmental education enhances the public's understanding of the need for biodiversity. Environmental education also educates the public about how their actions affect natural ecosystems and how positive steps taken to minimize impacts on these ecosystems will translate into improvements in our overall environment.

Status of Environmental Education

Environmental education is taking place across the country-in classrooms and board rooms, in living rooms and urban education centers, in city halls and chambers. How is it being done and who is doing it? What obstacles must we overcome to ensure that all citizens have the knowledge, skills, and attitudes to make informed decisions about the environment? What do professionals face in trying to create an environmentally literate citizenry?

Since 1970, a variety of educational institutions, environmental organizations, and government agencies have supported the development, delivery, and evaluation of environmental education in India. These environmental education efforts have targeted a variety of audiences, including teachers and students in elementary and secondary education, administrators at all levels, college and university teachers and students, adults and the general public, senior citizens, multi-ethnic communities, and political and business leaders. In general, current environmental education efforts generally fit into one of two sectors:

- Formal environmental education, which consists of activities taking place in elementary and secondary schools, colleges, universities, and technical institutions
- Nonformal environmental education, which includes activities taking place in businesses, nonprofit organizations,

and other institutions that are not considered part of the formal education system, also encompasses activities that involve the media, including newspapers, magazines, television, and computer networks.

Within each of these broad sectors, there are several sub-sectors that encompass the majority of environmental education activities taking place today. Collaboration between formal and nonformal sectors is common and widespread, from local nature centers working with school systems to government's agencies working with businesses and universities. Such collaboration is essential and it increases the reach and impact of environmental education programs.

Formal environmental education

Formal environmental education efforts focus on developing awareness, knowledge, skills, and motivation in students, teachers, and school administrators. Activities involve curriculum development; teacher and administrator training initiatives; local, state, and national school reform activities; evaluation; the development of national environmental education guidelines; and other related programs designed to improve elementary, secondary, and post-secondary education. The formal sector is commonly divide into activities for grades kindergarten through 12 and post-secondary education activities. However, there is overlap between the two, especially in regard to teacher training and curriculum development.

School environmental education activities

Delivery of environmental education programs in school education generally takes two approaches, with many school systems adopting some combination of the two. The most prevalent trend in elementary and secondary education is toward an approach called "infusion." This approach integrates environmental education into existing lessons, units, or topics focusing on other subjects such as history, science, and the social sciences. For example, students may learn how to solve a local environmental challenge-such as chemical contamination of a nearby stream-using scientific methods that include testing, identifying, and locating the source of contamination. Students may also learn how to solve this contamination problem by exploring historical dimensions for how this type of problem has been addressed in other communities, how governmental agencies can help, and how citizens can get involved. Ideally, infusion results in the incorporation of environmental education-an inherently interdisciplinary field-into all aspects of the curriculum at every grade level.

Infusion recognizes that environmental issues cut across disciplinary lines, and that environmental responsibility relies on knowledge, skills, and attitudes that incorporate, but also go beyond, basic scientific understanding. Because no one asks schools to do less-in fact, many demand they do more-infusion is a pragmatic approach to ensuring that environmental education can be incorporated into a crowded curriculum. But despite the arguments in favor of infusion, many environmental educators are wary.

Their concern is that environmental education may be short-changed or ignored unless it receives its own place in the curriculum. For this reason, many educators prefer the "second-course" or "block" approach. This approach consists of offering separate and distinct "environmental" courses.

Their argument is that the separate course approach can offer depth that is missing in the infusion approach, as well as an identifiable focus for attracting funding, evaluating progress, and encouraging career development.

According to recent data, most states rely on infusion as the main approach for integrating environmental education into the curriculum. However, more distinct environmental courses are being offered in middle and secondary schools, and many educators believe that this trend will continue. In addition, more schools are offering current events classes that include an environmental focus. The debate on how to incorporate environmental education continues. Both these approaches should complement one another and that efforts to choose an approach should be based on state, local, and individual priorities, needs, and training.

Post-secondary environmental education activities

At the college and university level, environmental education is addressed in a variety of ways; however, the effectiveness of these efforts varies from state to state, institution to institution, and course to course, just as it does at the school level. In general, universities and colleges emphasize the following strategies to help create environmentally literate citizens:

— *Preparing Students for Environmentally Related Careers:* Courses and programs are offered that prepare students for specific environmental careers, including environmental science, natural resource management, environmental design, environmental engineering, environmental planning, and environmental management. Many universities and colleges also offer degrees in environmental studies, which differ from more technical programs in that they are interdisciplinary and include both the natural sciences and the social sciences. A relatively small number of universities and colleges offer undergraduate and graduate degrees in environmental education, which are designed to train students for careers as professional environmental educators working in formal and nonformal settings.

— *Providing teachers with pre-service environmental education training:* These programs vary widely across the country. Some areas have very limited opportunities for student teachers to receive training in environmental education before they enter the classroom. On the other hand, some states, such as Wisconsin, have mandates requiring nearly all students training to become teachers to achieve environmental education competencies before being licensed to teach. In some institutions, students can take a specific environmental education or environmental studies course. In others, they receive environmental education content and methodologies through other courses-often in science or general methodology classes. Unfortunately, most environmental education training for teachers takes place after they leave the university and start teaching-as a result of in-service training or individual teacher initiative.

— *Providing environmental education training for all University and college students:* There is a growing trend among universities to include environmental education requirements for all students-not just those majoring in environmentally related fields. For example, Tufts University initiated an Environmental Literacy Institute for university professors from around the world to help them incorporate environmental education into all coursework, from creative writing to politics to law. This program was initiated in 1993 and has involved more than 150 universities and organizations from around the world. In addition, more than 250 universities and organizations have become signatories to the Talloires Declaration, which supports an interdisciplinary approach to environmental literacy at the university level.

— *Providing environmental education training for students majoring in business:* Another trend is the emergence of environmental management education in business schools across the country. Several business schools are currently incorporating environmental content into their curriculum, hoping to influence the attitudes and behavior of current and future business graduates regarding the link between a healthy economy and a healthy environment.

— *Conducting research and evaluation:* Universities and colleges have taken the lead in conducting a broad spectrum of environmental education research projects concerning environmental knowledge, skills, attitudes, and action. Findings have been published in a variety of periodicals, such as The Journal of Environmental

Education and in conference proceedings and monographs such as those produced by the North American Association for Environmental Education (NAAEE). Through NAAEE's North American Commission on Environmental Education Research, faculty from nearly 20 universities, including Rutgers University, Ohio State University, the University of Wisconsin-Stevens Point, and Northern Illinois University, have cooperated in identifying and addressing research needs in environmental education.

— *Environmental career training:* Community and technical colleges have become increasingly active in providing training programs in the environmental field, offering specific degree programs for such careers as water/wastewater technicians and course offerings on a variety of specific topics. At present, these programs focus mainly on technical aspects of job performance and regulatory compliance, but the opportunity exists for a broader environmental education approach that also encompasses the nature of the environmental challenges that prompted the need for regulation. Community colleges, in particular, provide a substantial resource for minority students, many of which graduate and attend universities for advanced degrees.

Links between school and post-secondary environmental education

A variety of environmental education activities taking place in the formal sector involve collaboration between university and college programs and the nation's elementary and secondary schools. They also involve collaboration with nonformal institutions, government agencies, and other institutions. For example, many universities and colleges are involved in developing environmental education curriculum for school, enhancing in-service training, and evaluating environmental education curriculum materials and training. And many nonprofit organizations, such as environmental organizations and community educational institutions, are involved in training teachers, developing supplementary environmental education materials, and conducting programs for parents, families, youth, and the public.

Non-formal environmental eduation

Nonformal environmental education activities take place in a variety of settings throughout the country-from zoos, museums, aquariums, nature centers, and science centers to parks, and community centers. Nonformal environmental education programs often complement and enhance formal education programs. In addition, many target adults, the general public, or families. And some are designed for specific adult audiences, such as senior citizens, public policy makers, business leaders, and women's groups.

The goals of nonformal environmental education programs are similar to those in the formal sector-developing environmentally literate young people and adults who have the knowledge, skills, and motivation to make informed decisions about the environment. Activities in this sector involve community action projects sponsored by business and nonformal education organizations; programs in local, state, and national parks, wildlife refuges, and other natural areas; television, radio, and other media programs focused on environmental issues and actions; and a variety of partnership programs designed to improve elementary, secondary, and post-secondary education. In many cases, nonformal environmental education activities are directed toward the solution of specific environmental challenges.

It should be recognized that in reaching adults, there is a potentially strong link between formal and nonformal education. Parents' awareness and understanding of environmental issues are frequently enhanced by their children's involvement in environmental education. As children become involved in the problem solving and action elements of effective environmental education, they frequently take these issues home and involve their parents in discussions about them.

One of the central challenges to nonformal environmental education is how best to reach a noncaptive, out-of-school audience with a meaningful and effective program. What kind of education program will prompt behavior change or commitment to get involved in local, national, and global environmental issues? To address this problem, environmental education efforts in the nonformal sector vary widely. Following is an overview of the approaches currently in use around the nation.

Using the media

Newspapers, magazines, television, movies, and other media can transmit messages to large audiences, and have been gaining popularity as a means for educating the public about environmental issues. There are many excellent examples of media-based environmental education, such as attempts to educate about recycling; however, media efforts face two major challenges. The first is assuring that environmental messages publicized as education really are education rather than hype or propaganda. The second challenge is assuring breadth and depth in examining complex environmental issues. Entertainment and the media often emphasize environmental awareness, rather than education that leads to personal, organizational, or community participation.

Targeting specific audiences

Many nonformal institutions are involved in programs and activities that target specific audiences such as senior citizens, culturally diverse students and adults, preschoolers, tourists, policy makers, and most often, the general public. In some communities, schools, businesses, and nonformal institutions collaborate to reach a specific target audience. Many community institutions offer continuing education programs for adults and families focusing on environmental topics, as well as after-school, summer, and weekend environmental education programs for young people. In addition, some churches, synagogues, and other religious institutions are involved in environmental education activities that link religion with environmental stewardship.

Developing supplementary materials

Many organizations and institutions, from government agencies to environmental nonprofit organizations and businesses, have developed supplementary environmental education materials that are used in schools and community settings. These materials include a wide range of topics and approaches, from those dealing with a single subject such as solid waste to those focusing on broad environmental themes such as sustainable development. Some are meant to supplement formal school curricula. Others are meant to be used with students and adults in nonformal settings. The quality of these supplementary materials varies greatly.

Training educators

Many school educators receive environmental education training as a result of in-service training that takes place after they begin teaching. Much of this training takes place through workshops at national, regional, or state environmental education conferences, or courses sponsored by local university outreach and extension programs, often in conjunction with nonformal partners, such as museums, zoos, or science centers. Many teachers also participate in specialized workshops, such as those offered by Project Learning Tree, World Resources Institute, World Wildlife Fund, and other nonprofit educational organizations. These courses and workshops often provide "continuing education units" or specific college credits that many teachers need to maintain certification to teach.

Many organizations, institutions, agencies, and communities offer environmental education programs. We can group them into the following sectors:

— state, local, and tribal governments
— nongovernmental organizations
— universities, colleges, schools and technical training institutes
— central government
— business, industry, and the media
— foundations

The following discussion provides an overview of the types of activities in each sector, including sample program highlights to demonstrate the broad spectrum of environmental education activities taking place across the country.

Role of State and local governments

State and local governments are influential forces in formal environmental education because of their responsibility for public education. In many states, curricula are determined at the state level. In other states, local governments or school districts play a substantial role in curriculum development. State and local funds are often used for teacher-training, evaluation, and materials development. Tribal governments often complement state and local efforts and play an important role in supporting environmental education programs.

During the 1970s, most state education agencies appointed environmental education coordinators to oversee efforts within the formal education system. Coordinators were involved in developing state guidelines, curriculum materials, and in-service training programs. However, during the 1980s most states followed the central lead by deemphasizing environmental education. As a result, the responsibilities of full-time coordinators often shifted to one or more individuals who were already burdened with other responsibilities. During this period, accomplishments related to environmental education often reflected the interests of individuals rather than a commitment from state or local governments.

In the 1990s, there has been a reemergence of environmental education as a state governmental priority, as evidenced by the increasing numbers of states with new legislative initiatives. In 1991, the University of Wisconsin-Stevens Point began the National Environmental Education Advancement Project (NEEAP) to help teams of education and environmental education leaders develop comprehensive state environmental education initiatives. In 1995-1996, NEEAP conducted a survey of all 50 states allowing them to develop a state-bystate and composite picture of environmental education programs. Also in 1995, a State Education and Environment Roundtable was established to serve as a resource to state education agencies working to integrate environmental education into K-12 curriculum and schools' educational reform efforts. The Roundtable was established with funding from the Pew Charitable Trusts and is administered by the Council of Chief State School Officers.

Whether through state mandates, state agency efforts, or some type of independent state associations, there is a strong logic for building support for environmental education on a systematic state-bystate basis that ultimately strengthens local program efforts.

Role of nongovernmental organizations (NGOs)

Nongovernmental organizations (NGOs) have been leaders in environmental education initiatives taking place in the formal and nonformal sector since environmental education began. In some cases, educational activities are directed toward the solution of specific environmental challenges or increasing awareness about national or global issues such as acid rain or ozone depletion. Many NGOs also are involved in curriculum development, teacher training, and evaluation. Programs take place at such diverse sites as zoos, museums, wildlife refuges, parks, and nature centers.

During the 1980s, a number of trends in nonformal environmental education emerged, which have continued into the 1990s. These include an emphasis on urban and rural environmental education, interactive traveling exhibits focusing on environmental issues, eco-tourism education packages, and family and adult-oriented outdoor education camps. These trends are expected to continue, based on market demand, available leisure time, and the spending countird's power.

NGOs include a variety of organizations, from nonprofit environmental groups, such as World Wildlife Fund and the National Environmnel Society, to professional associations that include environmental education activities.

A growing trend is the development of nongovernmental state environmental education associations or councils that provide an opportunity for strengthening state capacity for effective environmental education. Presently, 45 states have environmental education associations.

Formal educational institutions are actively involved in all aspects of environmental education, from in-service and preservice education to curriculum development and professional development.

Central Government

Many central agencies such as EPA, the Departments of Education, Interior, Agriculture, Energy, and State, the National Aeronautics and Space Administration (NASA), the National Oceanic and Atmospheric Administration (NOAA), the National Science Foundation, and the Peace Corps have ongoing environmental education programs tailored to the missions of their respective agencies.

Central support for environmental education includes teacher training, grants to support state and local projects and to promote equity and diversity across states, the development and dissemination of educational materials, as well as field and laboratory internship programs.

The environmental education programs can help the government meet its broader goals for supporting education reform; job creation, training, and economic competitiveness; public health; environmental protection; and sustainable development.

Increasingly, central agencies have been working together to set program priorities by serving on interagency advisory committees, review panels, and strategic planning sessions. In addition, central agencies have been increasingly collaborating on developing and implementing joint projects through interagency agreements. For example, in US, EPA and the Department of Education worked together to add a new priority to EPA's Environmental Education Grant Program which focuses on using environmental education as a catalyst to advance state and local education reform goals. In addition, NASA, the Department of Agriculture, the U.S. Global Change Research Program, EPA and others developed the "Global Change Education State Team Initiative" to improve literacy and teaching capability in global change education among educators and community leaders through statewide systemic education approaches.

Business and industry have become increasingly involved in supporting environmental education activities. Many companies have supported on-going environmental education programs or started their own to increase awareness about environmental issues and to help consumers understand the links between business and the environment.

Environmental messages are frequently appearing on everything from bottled water to paper bags, and advertisers are catering to "green" consumers by featuring the environmental advantages of one product over another. Amway, Chevron, Eastman Kodak, Phillips Petroleum, and Shell Oil are just a few examples of corporations that have conducted and supported environmental education activities for several years.

Environmental programming is also a regular feature on television, radio, video, computer networks, and other media outlets. The nonprofit Environmental Media Association (EMA) was founded in 1989 to foster the rapidly growing environmental interests of the entertainment industry.

EMA works with writers, producers, directors, and others to incorporate environmental themes into film, television, and music.Over the past five years, private charitable foundations have increased their funding for environmental education. Some, like the Pew Charitable Trusts, the Geraldine R. Dodge Foundation, and the Rockefeller Brothers Fund, have supported environmental education for many years.

Many foundation grants are typically for three years or less, are usually limited to $100,000 per year, and usually advance a single resource conservation program within the foundation's overall goals. For example in US, the two Congressionally-funded foundations in the field, the National Fish and Wildlife Foundation (NFWF) and the National Environmental Education and Training Foundation (NEETF), are making major contributions to environmental education. The matching grants awarded by NFWF and NEETF increase private support and partnerships for environmental education. Unlike endowment-based private foundations, these foundations are funded by annual central appropriations.

The number of foundations funding environmental projects is growing, and opportunities for environmental education are good. To increase their share of foundation support, the environmental education community will need to build a stronger connection between education and the environmental improvement goals of philanthropic foundations.

Issues and Challenges of Environmental Education

In the past several decades, central and state agencies; nongovernmental organizations; educational institutions; and others working at local, state, and national levels have developed a wide variety of effective environmental programs. Despite innumerable program accomplishments, the field of environmental education faces many challenges, as summarized below. However, it is important to note that environmental education is a long-term process that requires on-going support and participation from all sectors of society.

Environmental Education is not a priority across the country

Despite the wealth of programs and materials, widespread support and funding for environmental education is often lacking. Environmental education is not a clear priority at any level within our education system or society, and many programs face on-going resource, funding, and staff limitations. In addition, many view environmental education as an "add-on" and not part of mainstream education. For these reasons, there needs to be clear and consistent political and legislative support at all levels.

Many experts agree that despite many exemplary efforts, this lack of long-term consistent support and commitment at all levels has created a field that is often fragmented, inefficient, and duplicative. The Council recognizes that the National Environmental Education Act is a critical and needed step in stimulating national support for environmental education and a renewed central commitment for environmental education. However, much work still needs to be done at national, state, and local levels to institutionalize environmental education and make it a nationwide priority.

State, local, and tribal efforts need greater resources and support

Although consistent central leadership and commitment is critical to the success of environmental education in the United States, most environmental education initiatives are best developed and implemented at the state, local, and tribal levels.

The central government's primary role should be to support exemplary state, local, and tribal initiatives that have evolved over the last two decades. Central support can help institutionalize such programs and promote a sustainable environmental education infrastructure that will function despite shifts in spending priorities.

Many experts believe that the most effective way to enhance state and local capacity to implement effective programs is to support the development of comprehensive state environmental education programs that include statewide environmental education offices, state coordinators, and state coordinating councils. In some states, legislative mandates are the most effective means of institutionalizing environmental education efforts.

The Council of State Governments has developed "Model State Environmental Education Legislation" which can help states to explore this option. Alternative methods, including the creation of independent state environmental education councils or associations, that help serve as focal points for central, state, and local agencies, as well as nonprofit organizations, business, and industry, can also promote environmental education on a statewide basis.

Resources are linited and no one sector can support the entire field

Solutions to environmental issues require increased collaboration among all sectors of society-including business, industry, schools, community organizations, citizens, funding institutions, and government. In the past, the responsibility for environmental education rested mainly with nonprofit organizations, community educational institutions, and motivated educators scattered throughout the country.

With the passage of the National Environmental Education Act, there was hope that the central government would supply much of the needed funding. But the central government cannot supply the amount of funding needed to support the field; rather, it can help leverage support from state, local, and private sources.

Today, there are more partnerships and a better understanding that collaboration is the key to sustainability. Although models exist in almost every state, we need more partnerships that work-across central agencies, within EPA, among nonprofits, schools, and business, and between the public and private sectors. Specifically, business needs to get more involved-especially in supporting local and state environmental education efforts.

Central agencies and like-minded organizations need to collaborate on more projects of mutual interest to prevent waste and duplication. Zoos, museums, nature centers, and other community educational institutions need to work more closely with the formal education system and with parents and families.

There also is a need to build on existing international partnerships. Environmental challenges are global and will increasingly need international cooperation to find effective solutions. It is critical that countries establish and enhance mechanisms to share success stories and lessons learned to improve national and international environmental education efforts.

Professional development for teachers and nonformal educators needs greater support and improvement

Over the long term, one of the most cost-effective efforts that can be undertaken to improve environmental education in the United States is to improve the quality of pre-service and in-service teacher professional development, and training for instructors in environmental education programs outside the classroom. Although good programs exist, most experts agree that teacher and instructor training for environmental education is inconsistently available. Teachers often express misgivings about their competence to conduct environmental education programs and have limited opportunities for training before and after entering the classroom. Although some states require environmental education training, surveys indicate a notable lack of emphasis on environmental education in pre-service teacher training, as well as in-service instruction.

Environmental education is not well integrated into education reform and improvement

Environmental education has the potential to significantly improve the public education system. Many of the goals championed by education reform and improvement advocates-such as the need to strengthen interdisciplinary teaching and criticalthinking and problem-solving skills-can be effectively accomplished using environmental education as a vehicle. Although there are some good efforts under way, environmental education has not consistently been well integrated into education reform and improvement efforts across the country and it has not generally been identified as a priority of the formal education establishment. This is partly a reflection of the environmental education establishment's tendency in the past to focus more on reaching teachers and students rather than state education agencies, local school boards, principals and other school administrators. Consequently, key educational decision makers are not generally knowledgeable of the potential effectiveness of environmental education in achieving many of the basic goals of education reform.

Environmental education, by its nature, draws on and impacts many disciplines, such as science, math, history, and political science. It also is readily identifiable as a critical component of citizenship education, science literacy, career development, and a variety of other initiatives supported by the education reform movement. Education reform can be a mechanism for giving environmental education an established place in the curriculum, making it less subject to funding priority shifts and more likely to be a focus in teacher training.

Important audiences are not being reached

Most environmental education efforts have focused on elementary and secondary students-especially in kindergarten through the 6th grade-with some support in community colleges, vocational education, higher education and the Cooperative Extension Service. Important audiences in environmental education are being missed or inadequately reached, such as adults, people of color, low-income populations, and senior citizens. In part, this is due to lack of materials, commitment and organizational support; uncertainties in knowing how to engage these audiences; and difficulties in adapting traditional teaching strategies to nonformal learning environments within communities and diverse cultures. Environmental education materials are rarely available in languages other than English, although some have been translated into Spanish, and such materials are not always sensitive to diverse cultures.

Evaluation, quality assurance, and access to materials and information on programmes is limited

What works in environmental education? What types of training programs for teachers and nonformal educators and which environmental education materials are most effective and why? What does it mean to be environmentally literate? How do educators gain greater access to quality materials? Where are the gaps in materials and programs?

In general, environmental education programs have not received rigorous evaluation to determine their effectiveness. Several factors have contributed to this, including limited funding to undertake short and longterm evaluations, difficulty in identifying quantitative objectives, and the complexity of measuring long-term educational changes. Experts agree that the field needs more baseline data to evaluate current and future environmental education efforts and to ensure that the highest quality programs and projects are funded and implemented. There is a need for research on methods, materials, and effectiveness; evaluation components for all programs and projects funded; and the establishment of guidelines for program and material evaluation.

In addition, the field has had limited resources to develop nationally accepted guidelines to help practitioners assess the value and effectiveness of both formal and nonformal environmental education methods, materials, and programs, as well as nationally accepted learner outcomes to indicate what a student should know when he or she graduates from high school or national guidelines for teacher training programs. To fill this need, the North American Association for Environmental Education (NAAEE) is currently working with EPA and a variety of educational organizations and agencies across the country to develop environmental education guidelines that focus on three areas:

— materials development

— learner outcomes

— environmental educator competencies

These guidelines will be consistent with guidelines developed for major disciplines, especially with science and geography guidelines. Access to high quality environmental education materials and programs varies from community to community, and from state to state. In some cases, appropriate materials and programs do not exist-especially for specific audiences, such as urban educators, senior citizens, adults, people of color, and culturallydiverse communities. In other cases, access to existing materials and programs is limited because of limitations in funding and "user-friendly" mechanisms for finding out about new and existing materials and programs.

Another related issue is the proliferation of materials that are duplicative of existing curricula materials and have ineffective implementation strategies. In some cases, the problem for teachers is not access to quality materials, but lack of training in how to effectively use available materials. In other cases, the problem is how to best evaluate and select the most effective and educationally sound materials from the many materials that exist.

Identifying existing gaps in current environmental education materials and programs is another critical issue. Many materials and programs emphasize awareness, appreciation, and knowledge, without a focus on skill development and commitment to informed and responsible action. While it is critical that all environmental education efforts have a sound basis in science, there is a disproportionate emphasis in formal education on science-oriented activities at the expense of other subject areas such as geography and civics. Most curriculum materials developed for K-12 have a very limited topical focus, such as water pollution, resource use/recycling, or energy.

Environmental education should be interdisciplinary, with a focus on the learning process and not limited to only one or two specific issues. Experts feel that the field needs to develop a more balanced menu of materials and programs that emphasize skill development and citizen participation, and that stress the interdisciplinary nature of environmental issues.

More well-trained environmental professionals are needed

To tackle current and future environmental challenges, experts in the private and public sectors agree that we need a better-trained cadre of environmental professionals-from highly skilled scientists and engineers to city planners and technicians. The environmental work force is especially lacking in representation from communities of people of color.

Universities, community colleges, vocational schools, and other training institutions need to offer more training opportunities in environmental studies, environmental design, environmental engineering, environmental management, conservation biology, and other related courses of study. At the same time, environmental education should be infused into traditional coursework to produce lawyers, business leaders, and planners with the knowledge, skills, and ethic to make informed and responsible decisions about the environment. Unfortunately, many of today's courses lack the interdisciplinary ties that link pure sciences with the social sciences.

Current efforts to provide environmental career opportunities are limited-especially for people of color and students with low incomes. Positive partnerships, among businesses, nonprofits, government, and schools, have increased the number of internships, fellowships, and apprenticeship programs available to students, but many more are needed to meet current and future demands. The challenge is to attract more bright, motivated students to the field and to provide high-quality, interdisciplinary education to all learners.

2

Environmental Pollution

Environmental pollution is a term that refers to all the ways that human activity harms the natural environment. The major types of environmental pollution include air pollution, water pollution, soil pollution, pollution caused by solid waste and hazardous waste, and noise pollution. The relationships among all the living and nonliving things in an environment make up an ecological system, called an ecosystem. All the ecosystems of the Earth are connected. Thus, pollution that seems to affect only one part of the environment may also affect other parts.

Air pollution is the contamination of the air by various substances. Most of this pollution results from the burning of fuel to power motor vehicles and heat buildings. Chemicals called chlorofluorocarbons (CFC's) used in refrigerators and air conditioners and to make plastic foam insulation are pollutants that destroy the ozone layer in the upper atmosphere.

The burning of rubbish may discharge smoke and heavy metals, such as lead and mercury, into the atmosphere. Most heavy metals are highly poisonous. Forest fires and volcanic eruptions shoot gases and particulates into the atmosphere, and rain and wind wash them out or scatter them.

Water pollution is the contamination of water by sewage, toxic chemicals, metals, oils, or other substances. It can affect such surface waters as rivers, lakes, and oceans, as well as the water beneath the earth's surface, called ground water. Another form of water pollution is the clean but heated water discharged by power plants into waterways. This heated water, called thermal pollution, harms fish and aquatic plants by reducing the amount of oxygen in the water. Chemical and oil spills can also cause devastating water pollution that kills water birds, shellfish, and other wildlife.

Soil pollution is the destruction of the Earth's thin layer of healthy, productive soil, where much of our food is grown. Farmers who overuse fertilizers and pesticides can destroy their soil's productivity. Mining operations and smelters contaminate soil with toxic heavy metals. Many scientists believe acid rain can also reduce soil fertility. Solid waste from homes, offices, and stores is called municipal solid waste. It includes paper, plastic, bottles and cans, food scraps, and garden trimmings. Other waste consists of discarded furniture, scrapped cars, scrap metal, leftover materials from agricultural processes, and mining wastes known as spoil. The uncontrolled burning of solid waste creates smoke and other air pollution. Even burning waste in incinerators can release toxic chemicals, ash, and harmful metals into the air.

Hazardous waste is composed of discarded substances that can threaten human health and the environment. These pollutants include radiation, pesticides, and heavy metals. Radioactive waste produced by nuclear reactors and weapons factories pose a potentially serious environmental problem. Some of this waste will remain radioactive for thousands of years. The safe storage of radioactive waste is both difficult and expensive. When buried in the ground or left in open dumps, some hazardous waste can pollute ground water and contaminate food crops.

Noise pollution comes from such machines as aeroplanes, motor vehicles, construction machinery, and industrial equipment. Noise does not dirty the air, water, or land, but it can cause discomfort and hearing loss in human beings and other animals.

Environmental pollution is one of the most serious problems facing humanity and other life forms on our planet today. Nearly everyone would like to have pollution reduced. Unfortunately, most of the pollution that now threatens the health of our planet comes from products that many people want and need. Controlling pollution depends on the efforts of governments, scientists, business and industry, agriculture, environmental organizations, and individuals. The most important way people can fight pollution is to learn as much as possible about how their actions affect the environment. Then they can make intelligent choices that will reduce damage to the planet. Over time, pollution can be reduced in many ways without seriously disrupting people's lives.

Pollution, contamination of Earth's environment with materials that interfere with human health, the quality of life, or the natural functioning of ecosystems (living organisms and their physical surroundings). Although some environmental pollution is a result of natural causes such as volcanic eruptions, most is caused by human activities.

There are two main categories of polluting materials, or pollutants. Biodegradable pollutants are materials, such as sewage, that rapidly decompose by natural processes. These pollutants become a problem when added to the environment faster than they can decompose. Nondegradable pollutants are materials that either do not decompose or decompose slowly in the natural environment. Once contamination occurs, it is difficult or impossible to remove these pollutants from the environment.

Nondegradable compounds such as dichlorodiphenyltrichloroethane (DDT), dioxins, polychlorinated biphenyls (PCBs), and radioactive materials can reach dangerous levels of accumulation as they are passed up the food chain into the bodies of progressively larger animals. For example, molecules of toxic compounds may collect on the surface of aquatic plants without doing much damage to the plants. A small fish that grazes on these plants accumulates a high concentration of the toxin. Larger fish or other carnivores that eat the small fish will accumulate even greater, and possibly life-threatening, concentrations of the compound. This process is known as bioaccumulation.

IMPACTS OF POLLUTION

Because humans are at the top of the food chain, they are particularly vulnerable to the effects of nondegradable pollutants. This was clearly illustrated in the 1950s and 1960s when residents living near Minamata Bay, Japan, developed nervous disorders, tremors, and paralysis in a mysterious epidemic. More than 400 people died before authorities discovered that a local industry had released mercury into Minamata Bay. This highly toxic element accumulated in the bodies of local fish and eventually in the bodies of people who consumed the fish. More recently research has revealed that many chemical pollutants, such as DDT and PCBs, mimic sex hormones and interfere with the human body's reproductive and developmental functions. These substances are known as endocrine disrupters.

Occupational and environmental diseases

Pollution also has a dramatic effect on natural resources. Ecosystems such as forests, wetlands, coral reefs, and rivers perform many important services for Earth's environment. They enhance water and air quality, provide habitat for plants and animals, and provide food and medicines. Any or all of these ecosystem functions may be impaired or destroyed by pollution. Moreover, because of the complex relationships among the many types of organisms and ecosystems, environmental contamination may have far-reaching consequences that are not immediately obvious or that are difficult to predict. For instance, scientists can only speculate on some of the potential impacts of the depletion of the ozone layer, the protective layer in the atmosphere that shields Earth from the Sun's harmful ultraviolet rays.

Another major effect of pollution is the tremendous cost of pollution cleanup and prevention. The global effort to control emissions of carbon dioxide, a gas produced from the combustion of fossil fuels such as coal or oil, or of other organic materials like wood, is one such example.

The cost of maintaining annual national carbon dioxide emissions at 1990 levels is estimated to be 2 percent of the gross domestic product for developed countries. Expenditures to reduce pollution in the United States in 1993 totaled $109 billion: $105.4 billion on reduction, $1.9 billion on regulation, and $1.7 billion on research and development. Twenty-nine percent of the total cost went toward air pollution, 36 percent to water pollution, and 36 percent to solid waste management. In addition to its effects on the economy, health, and natural resources, pollution has social implications.

Research has shown that low-income populations and minorities do not receive the same protection from environmental contamination as do higher-income communities. Toxic waste incinerators, chemical plants, and solid waste dumps are often located in low-income communities because of a lack of organized, informed community involvement in municipal decision-making processes.

TYPES OF POLLUTION

Pollution exists in many forms and affects many different aspects of Earth's environment. Point-source pollution comes from specific, localized, and identifiable sources, such as sewage pipelines or industrial smokestacks. Nonpoint-source pollution comes from dispersed or uncontained sources, such as contaminated water runoff from urban areas or automobile emissions. The effects of these pollutants may be immediate or delayed.

Primary effects of pollution occur immediately after contamination occurs, such as the death of marine plants and wildlife after an oil spill at sea.

Secondary effects may be delayed or may persist in the environment into the future, perhaps going unnoticed for many years. DDT, a nondegradable compound, seldom poisons birds immediately, but gradually accumulates in their bodies. Birds with high concentrations of this pesticide lay thin-shelled eggs that fail to hatch or produce deformed offspring. These secondary effects, publicized by Rachel Carson in her 1962 book, Silent Spring, threatened the survival of species such as the bald eagle and peregrine falcon, and aroused public concern over the hidden effects of nondegradable chemical compounds.

Air pollution

Human contamination of Earth's atmosphere can take many forms and has existed since humans first began to use fire for agriculture, heating, and cooking. During the Industrial Revolution of the 18th and 19th centuries, however, air pollution became a major problem. As early as 1661 British author and founding member of the British Royal Society John Evelyn reported of London in his treatise Fumifugium, "... the weary Traveller, at many Miles distance, sooner smells, than sees the City to which he repairs. This is that pernicious Smoake which fullyes all her Glory, superinducing a sooty Crust or Furr upon all that it lights...."

Urban air pollution is commonly known as smog. The dark London smog that Evelyn wrote of is generally a smoky mixture of carbon monoxide and organic compounds from incomplete combustion (burning) of fossil fuels such as coal, and sulfur dioxide from impurities in the fuels. As the smog ages and reacts with oxygen, organic and sulfuric acids condense as droplets, increasing the haze. Smog developed into a major health hazard by the 20th century. In 1948, 19 people died and thousands were sickened by smog in the small U.S. steel-mill town of Donora, Pennsylvania. In 1952, about 4,000 Londoners died of its effects.

A second type of smog, photochemical smog, began reducing air quality over large cities like Los Angeles in the

1930s. This smog is caused by combustion in car, truck, and airplane engines, which produce nitrogen oxides and release hydrocarbons from unburned fuels. Sunlight causes the nitrogen oxides and hydrocarbons to combine and turn oxygen into ozone, a chemical agent that attacks rubber, injures plants, and irritates lungs.

The hydrocarbons are oxidized into materials that condense and form a visible, pungent haze. Eventually most pollutants are washed out of the air by rain, snow, fog, or mist, but only after traveling large distances, sometimes across continents. As pollutants build up in the atmosphere, sulfur and nitrogen oxides are converted into acids that mix with rain. This acid rain falls in lakes and on forests, where it can lead to the death of fish and plants, and damage entire ecosystems.

Eventually the contaminated lakes and forests may become lifeless. Regions that are downwind of heavily industrialized areas, such as Europe and the eastern United States and Canada, are the hardest hit by acid rain. Acid rain can also affect human health and man-made objects; it is slowly dissolving historic stone statues and building facades in London, Athens, and Rome. One of the greatest challenges caused by air pollution is global warming, an increase in Earth's temperature due to the buildup of certain atmospheric gases such as carbon dioxide. With the heavy use of fossil fuels in the 20th century, atmospheric concentrations of carbon dioxide have risen dramatically.

Carbon dioxide and other gases, known as greenhouse gases, reduce the escape of heat from the planet without blocking radiation coming from the Sun. Because of this greenhouse effect, average global temperatures are expected to rise 1.4 to 5.8 Celsius degrees (2.5 to 10.4 Fahrenheit degrees) by the year 2100. Although this trend appears to be a small change, the increase would make the Earth warmer than it has been in the last 125,000 years, possibly changing climate patterns, affecting crop production, disrupting wildlife distributions, and raising the sea level.

Air pollution can also damage the upper atmospheric region known as the stratosphere. Excessive production of chlorine-containing compounds such as chlorofluorocarbons (CFCs) (compounds formerly used in refrigerators, air conditioners, and in the manufacture of polystyrene products) has depleted the stratospheric ozone layer, creating a hole above Antarctica that lasts for several weeks each year. As a result, exposure to the Sun's harmful rays has damaged aquatic and terrestrial wildlife and threatens human health in high-latitude regions of the northern and southern hemispheres.

WATER POLLUTION

The demand for fresh water rises continuously as the world's population grows. From 1940 to 1990 withdrawals of fresh water from rivers, lakes, reservoirs, and other sources increased fourfold. Of the water consumed in the United States in 1995, 39 percent was used for irrigation, 39 percent was used for electric power generation, and 12 percent was used for other utilities; industry and mining used 7 percent, and the rest was used for agricultural livestock and commercial purposes.

Sewage, industrial wastes, and agricultural chemicals such as fertilizers and pesticides are the main causes of water pollution. The U.S. Environmental Protection Agency (EPA) reports that about 37 percent of the country's lakes and estuaries, and 36 percent of its rivers, are too polluted for basic uses such as fishing or swimming during all or part of the year. In developing nations, more than 95 percent of urban sewage is discharged untreated into rivers and bays, creating a major human health hazard. Water runoff, a nonpoint source of pollution, carries fertilizing chemicals such as phosphates and nitrates from agricultural fields and yards into lakes, streams, and rivers.

These combine with the phosphates and nitrates from sewage to speed the growth of algae, a type of plantlike organism. The water body may then become choked with decaying algae, which severely depletes the oxygen supply. This process, called eutrophication, can cause the death of fish and other aquatic life. Agricultural runoff may be to blame for the growth of a toxic form of algae called Pfiesteria piscicida, which was responsible for killing large amounts of fish in bodies of water from the Delaware Bay to the Gulf of Mexico in the late 1990s. Runoff also carries toxic pesticides and urban and industrial wastes into lakes and streams.

Erosion, the wearing away of topsoil by wind and rain, also contributes to water pollution. Soil and silt (a fine sediment) washed from logged hillsides, plowed fields, or construction sites, can clog waterways and kill aquatic vegetation. Even small amounts of silt can eliminate desirable fish species. For example, when logging removes the protective plant cover from hillsides, rain may wash soil and silt into streams, covering the gravel beds that trout or salmon use for spawning.

The marine fisheries supported by ocean ecosystems are an essential source of protein, particularly for people in developing countries. Yet pollution in coastal bays, estuaries, and wetlands threatens fish stocks already depleted by overfishing. In 1989, 260,000 barrels of oil was spilled from the oil tanker Exxon Valdez into Alaska's Prince William Sound, a pristine and rich fishing ground. In 1999 there were 8,539 reported spills in and around U.S. waters, involving 4.4 billion liters (1.2 billion gallons) of oil.

Soil pollution

Soil is a mixture of mineral, plant, and animal materials that forms during a long process that may take thousands of years. It is necessary for most plant growth and is essential for all agricultural production. Soil pollution is a buildup of toxic chemical compounds, salts, pathogens, or radioactive materials that can affect plant and animal life. Unhealthy soil management methods have seriously degraded soil quality, caused soil pollution, and enhanced erosion.

Treating the soil with chemical fertilizers, pesticides, and fungicides interferes with the natural processes occurring within the soil and destroys useful organisms such as bacteria, fungi, and other microorganisms. For instance, strawberry farmers in California fumigate the soil with methyl bromide to destroy organisms that may harm young strawberry plants. This process indiscriminately kills even beneficial microorganisms and leaves the soil sterile and dependent upon fertilizer to support plant growth. This results in heavy fertilizer use and increases polluted runoff into lakes and streams.

Improper irrigation practices in areas with poorly drained soil may result in salt deposits that inhibit plant growth and may lead to crop failure. In 2000 bc, the ancient Sumerian cities of the southern Tigris-Euphrates Valley in Mesopotamia depended on thriving agriculture. By 1500 bc, these cities had collapsed largely because of crop failure due to high soil salinity. The same soil pollution problem exists today in the Indus Valley in Pakistan, the Nile Valley in Egypt, and the Imperial Valley in California.

Solid waste

Solid wastes are unwanted solid materials such as garbage, paper, plastics and other synthetic materials, metals, and wood. Billions of tons of solid waste are thrown out annually. The United States alone produces about 200 million metric tons of municipal solid waste each year. A typical American generates an average of 2 kg of solid waste each day. Cities in economically developed countries produce far more solid waste per capita than those in developing countries. Moreover, waste from developed countries typically contains a high percentage of synthetic materials that take longer to decompose than the primarily biodegradable waste materials of developing countries.

Areas where wastes are buried, called landfills, are the cheapest and most common disposal method for solid wastes worldwide. But landfills quickly become overfilled and may contaminate air, soil, and water. Incineration, or burning, of waste reduces the volume of solid waste but produces dense ashen wastes that often contain dangerous concentrations of hazardous materials such as heavy metals and toxic compounds.

Composting, using natural biological processes to speed the decomposition of organic wastes, is an effective strategy for dealing with organic garbage and produces a material that can be used as a natural fertilizer. Recycling, extracting and reusing certain waste materials, has become an important part of municipal solid waste strategies in developed countries. According to the EPA, more than one-fourth of the municipal solid waste produced in the United States is now recycled or composted. Recycling also plays a significant, informal role in solid waste management for many Asian countries, such as India, where organized waste-pickers comb streets and dumps for items such as plastics, which they use or resell.

Expanding recycling programs worldwide can help reduce solid waste pollution, but the key to solving severe solid waste problems lies in reducing the amount of waste generated. Waste prevention, or source reduction, such as altering the way products are designed or manufactured to make them easier to reuse, reduces the high costs associated with environmental pollution.

Hazardous waste

Hazardous wastes are solid, liquid, or gas wastes that may be deadly or harmful to people or the environment and tend to be persistent or nondegradable in nature. Such wastes include toxic chemicals and flammable or radioactive substances, including industrial wastes from chemical plants or nuclear reactors, agricultural wastes such as pesticides and fertilizers, medical wastes, and household hazardous wastes such as toxic paints and solvents.

About 400 million metric tons of hazardous wastes are generated each year. The United States alone produces about

250 million metric tons—70 percent from the chemical industry. The use, storage, transportation, and disposal of these substances pose serious environmental and health risks. Even brief exposure to some of these materials can cause cancer, birth defects, nervous system disorders, and death. Large-scale releases of hazardous materials may cause thousands of deaths and contaminate air, water, and soil for many years. The world's worst nuclear reactor accident took place near Chernobyl', Ukraine, in 1986.

The accident killed at least 31 people, forced the evacuation and relocation of more than 200,000 more, and sent a plume of radioactive material into the atmosphere that contaminated areas as far away as Norway and the United Kingdom. Until the Minamata Bay contamination was discovered in Japan in the 1960s and 1970s, most hazardous wastes were legally dumped in solid waste landfills, buried, or dumped into lakes, rivers, and oceans. Legal regulations now restrict how such materials may be used or disposed, but such laws are difficult to enforce and often contested by industry. It is not uncommon for industrial firms in developed countries to pay poorer countries to accept shipments of solid and hazardous wastes, a practice that has become known as the waste trade.

Moreover, cleaning up the careless dumping of the mid-20th century is costing billions of dollars and progressing very slowly, if at all. The United States has an estimated 217,000 hazardous waste dumps that need immediate action. Cleaning them up could take more than 30 years and cost $187 billion. Hazardous wastes of particular concern are the radioactive wastes from the nuclear power and weapons industries. To date there is no safe method for permanent disposal of old fuel elements from nuclear reactors. Most are kept in storage facilities at the original reactor sites where they were generated. With the end of the Cold War, nuclear warheads that are decommissioned, or no longer in use, also pose storage and disposal problems.

Noise pollution

Unwanted sound, or noise, such as that produced by airplanes, traffic, or industrial machinery, is considered a form of pollution. Noise pollution is at its worst in densely populated areas. It can cause hearing loss, stress, high blood pressure, sleep loss, distraction, and lost productivity.

Sounds are produced by objects that vibrate at a rate that the ear can detect. This rate is called frequency and is measured in hertz, or vibrations per second. Most humans can hear sounds between 20 and 20,000 hertz, while dogs can hear high-pitched sounds up to 50,000 hertz. While high-frequency sounds tend to be more hazardous and more annoying to hearing than low-frequency sounds, most noise pollution damage is related to the intensity of the sound, or the amount of energy it has.

Measured in decibels, noise intensity can range from zero, the quietest sound the human ear can detect, to over 160 decibels. Conversation takes place at around 40 decibels, a subway train is about 80 decibels, and a rock concert is from 80 to 100 decibels. The intensity of a nearby jet taking off is about 110 decibels. The threshold for pain, tissue damage, and potential hearing loss in humans is 120 decibels. Long-lasting, high-intensity sounds are the most damaging to hearing and produce the most stress in humans.

Solutions to noise pollution include adding insulation and sound-proofing to doors, walls, and ceilings; using ear protection, particularly in industrial working areas; planting vegetation to absorb and screen out noise pollution; and zoning urban areas to maintain a separation between residential areas and zones of excessive noise.

Radiation Pollution

The environmental problems of the Nuclear Age are concerned with radioactive fallout, both local as well as global and the consequent threat of environmental pollution.

Radioactive fallout means the deposition of air-borne radioactive contamination on the earth. Radioactive substances can enter the body through inhalation, through contaminated food and drinks, and through wounds and abrasions on the skin. When people are exposed to radiation there is bodily damage to them as well as impairment of the health of even their descendants. Apart from fallout, radiation sickness may be caused by x-ray machines.

Pollution results from radiation as well; hence warning labels are attached. During World War II, the U.S. dropped the first atomic bombs on the Japanese cities of Hiroshima and Nagasaki injuring and killing thousands of people. When a radioactive substance gets deposited in the body, it causes delayed effects, which may include skin cancer, leukemia and stunted growth.

THE INCREASE OF POLLUTION : FROM ANCIENT PERIOD TO TODAY

Much of what we know of ancient civilizations comes from the wastes they left behind. Refuse such as animal skeletons and implements from stone age cave dwellings in Europe, China, and the Middle East helps reveal hunting techniques, diet, clothing, tool usage, and the use of fire for cooking. Prehistoric refuse heaps, or middens, discovered by archaeologists in coastal areas of North America reveal information about the shellfish diet and eating habits of Native Americans who lived more than 10,000 years ago. As humans developed new technologies, the magnitude and severity of pollution increased.

Many historians speculate that the extensive use of lead plumbing for drinking water in Rome caused chronic lead poisoning in those who could afford such plumbing. The mining and smelting of ores that accompanied the transition from the Stone Age to the Metal Age resulted in piles of mining wastes that spread potentially toxic elements such as mercury, copper, lead, and nickel throughout the environment. Evidence of pollution during the early Industrial Revolution is widespread.

Samples of hair from historical figures such as Newton and Napoleon show the presence of toxic elements such as antimony and mercury. By the 1800s, certain trades were associated with characteristic occupational diseases: Chimney sweeps contracted cancer of the scrotum from hydrocarbons in chimney soot; hatters became disoriented, or "mad," from nerve-destroying mercury salts used to treat felt fabric; and bootblacks suffered liver damage from boot polish solvents.

During the 20th century, pollution evolved from a mainly localized problem to one of global consequences in which pollutants not only persisted in the environment, but changed atmospheric and climatic conditions. The Minamata Bay disaster was the first major indication that humans would need to pay more attention to their waste products and waste disposal practices, in particular, hazardous waste disposal. In the years that followed, many more instances of neglect or carelessness resulted in dangerous levels of contamination.

In 1976 an explosion at a chemical factory in Seveso, Italy, released clouds of toxic dioxin into the area, exposing hundreds of residents and killing thousands of animals that ate exposed food. In 1978 it was discovered that the Love Canal housing development in New York State was built on a former chemical waste dump. The development was declared uninhabitable. The world's worst industrial accident occurred in Bhopal, India, in 1984. A deadly gas leaked from an American chemical plant, killing more than 3,800 people and injuring more than 200,000.

The 1986 Chernobyl' nuclear reactor accident demonstrated the dangerous contamination effects of large, uncontained disasters. In an unprecedented action, pollution was used as a military tactic in 1991 during the conflict in the Persian Gulf. The Iraqi military intentionally released as much as 1 billion liters (336 million gallons) of crude oil into the Persian Gulf and set fire to more than 700 oil wells, sending thick, black smoke into the atmosphere over the Middle East.

METHODS TO CHECK POLLUTION

People all over the world have realized the harmful effects of Pollution. Various approaches have been adopted in order to counter the effects of pollution.

i) *Recycling:* The process of reprocessing waste products so that they can be used again is known as recycling. Things like cans and paper can be broken down and used again for the same purpose. Things like old tyres can be melted down using special methods to give chemicals like oil and gas.

ii) *Technological developments:* Filters or Catalytic Converters are used in vehicles to remove the pollutants from the exhaust and to make the process of combustion more complete. In the case of agriculture, biological controls are being used instead of pesticides. In this method different kinds of insects and bacteria are used to control pests.

iii) *Restrictions:* Limitations have been put on the use of products like the DDT. A lot of cars today use unleaded petrol, as the lead present in the car exhausts is one of the major causes of Pollution. More and more car manufacturers are being encouraged to build machines that do not require leaded petrol.

iv) *Organizations controlling pollution:* The most in influential organization in favor of a pollution free world is the Greenpeace organization. The organization was founded in Canada in 1971. The main aim of this international organization is to protect the environment. Greenpeace draws the attention of the people towards activities like, oil drilling, nuclear bomb testing and the dumping of wastes Into the ocean, which can cause grave danger to the environment. The organization also supports issues like, the threat to wild life because of hunting, the threat to wild life caused by habitat loss. The methods used by the members of the group is always direct and non-violent. If they come to know of any activity which they think is harmful to the environment, they reach the particular site and try to stop the activity.

In the span of the entire World History, the last century has been the most dynamic therefore remarkable century. Unprecedented breakthroughs have occurred in all spheres of human interest intellectual, scientific, health, political and religious. Never has conventional thought or theories been subjected to a more critical and skeptical perspective. The level of development of communication has turned the world into a global village. And the pace at which research and development is occurring in every field, more inventions and discoveries are bound to emerge in the future.

Along with the major concerns of the present age: health, poverty, human rights and environment, the threat of war is becoming an issue of worldwide concern. We expect that humanity would learn the lessons that history has to offer, so that the dangers and blunders can be avoided in the present. But this has not always been the case. There was a Second World War although the world had witnessed the devastation of the

First. And yet, man today has acquired the potential (nuclear, atomic and biological weapons) to destroy the Earth, not once but many times over! Military aggression and international terrorism is rising in alarming proportions. Looking at these developments one cannot deny the possibility of another world war. Isn't it ironic that today when we boast of being most "civilized" and "modern," the nations of the world have not even been able to come up with a consensus to arrest the production of arms that can threaten the very existence of humanity?

CONTROLLING POLLUTION

Because of the many environmental tragedies of the mid-20th century, many nations instituted comprehensive regulations designed to repair the past damage of uncontrolled pollution and prevent future environmental contamination. In the United States, the Clean Air Act and its amendments significantly reduced certain types of air pollution, such as sulfur dioxide emissions. The Clean Water Act and Safe Drinking Water Act regulated pollution discharges and set water quality standards.

The Toxic Substances Control Act and the Resource Conservation and Recovery Act provided for the testing and control of toxic and hazardous wastes. In 1980 Congress passed the Comprehensive Environmental Response, Compensation, and Liability Act (CERCLA), also known as Superfund, to provide funds to clean up the most severely contaminated hazardous waste sites. These and several other federal and state laws helped limit uncontrolled pollution, but progress has been slow and many severe contamination problems remain due to lack of funds for cleanup and enforcement.

International agreements have also played a role in reducing global pollution. The Montreal Protocol on Substances that Deplete the Ozone Layer set international target dates for reducing the manufacture and emissions of the chemicals, such as CFCs, known to deplete the ozone layer. The Basel Convention on the Control of Transboundary Movements of Hazardous Wastes and Their Disposal serves as a framework for the international regulation of hazardous waste transport and disposal.

Since 1992 representatives from more than 160 nations have met regularly to discuss methods to reduce greenhouse gas emissions. In 1997 the Kyoto Protocol was devised, calling for industrialized countries to reduce their gas emissions by 2012 to an average 5 percent below 1990 levels. At the end of 2000 the Kyoto Protocol had not yet been ratified; negotiators were still working to find consensus on the rules, methods, and penalties that should be used to enforce the treaty. Regulations and legislation have led to considerable progress in cleaning up air and water pollution in developed countries. Vehicles in the 1990s emit fewer nitrogen oxides than those in the 1970s did; power plants now burn low-sulfur fuels; industrial stacks have scrubbers to reduce emissions; and lead has been removed from gasoline.

Developing countries, however, continue to struggle with pollution control because they lack clean technologies and desperately need to improve economic strength, often at the cost of environmental quality. The problem is compounded by developing countries attracting foreign investment and industry by offering cheaper labor, cheaper raw materials, and fewer environmental restrictions.

The maquiladoras, assembly plants along the Mexican side of the Mexico-U.S. border, provide jobs and industry for Mexico but are generally owned by non-Mexican corporations attracted to the cheap labor and lack of pollution regulation. As a result, this border region, including the Río Grande, is one of the most heavily polluted zones in North America. To avoid ecological disaster and increased poverty, developing countries will require aid and technology from outside nations and corporations, community participation in development initiatives, and strong environmental regulations.

Nongovernmental citizen groups have formed at the local, national, and international level to combat pollution problems worldwide. Many of these organizations provide information and support for people or organizations traditionally not involved in the decision-making process. The Pesticide Action Network provides technical information about the effects of pesticides on farmworkers. The Citizen's Clearinghouse for Hazardous Waste, established by veterans of the Love Canal controversy, provides support for communities targeted for hazardous waste installations. A well-organized, grassroots, environmental justice movement has arisen to advocate equitable environmental protections.

Greenpeace is an activist organization that focuses international attention on industries and governments known to contaminate land, sea, or atmosphere with toxic or solid wastes. Friends of the Earth International is a federation of international organizations that fight environmental pollution around the world. A pollutant is any solid, liquid or gaseous substance present in such a concentration, so as to be injurious to the environment. Some of the common pollutants in developed as well as developing countries are : gaseous pollutants such as oxides of nitrogen, fluoride compounds, metals like mercury and lead, complex organic pollutants like benzene, petrochemical oxidants like ethylene, deposited matter like smoke and soot, solid waste, poisons like herbicides and fungicides, fertilizers, radioactive waste, noise and heat.

From the point of view of the ecosystem, pollutants may be classified as nondegradable pollutants like aluminum cans and DDT which do not degrade or degrade only very slowly in the environment, and biodegradable pollutants like domestic sewage which gets decomposed rapidly. Pollution may also occur naturally in the environment.

Adverse effects are noticed on plants since agriculture and horticulture are both affected by pollution. Air pollutants produce eye and respiratory irritation in animals and also in humans. Water pollutants can endanger aquatic life thus millions of fish are reported killed by municipal and industrial wastes. Sewage, toxic chemicals, and diseases causing germs can also make water unfit for farm animals. Thermal pollution, namely excessive heating of water in rivers or lakes can kill fish. Many diseases are water borne. Water pollutants like suspended particles can also adversely affect industrial equipment.

Air pollution is regarded as the most dangerous and common kind of environment pollution in recent times. The Bhopal Gas Tragedy in 1984 is regarded as the worst industrial accident, related to air pollution. Around two lakh Bhopal residents were affected by the leak of poisonous MIC gas from the Union Carbide Pesticide plant in Bhopal (India).

3

Causes and Effects of Environmental Hazards

Improving health requires understanding how environmental conditions foster disease. While the causal connections are clear for some diseases and conditions, for others scientific evidence can only identify associations and likely contributors. This section focuses on both biological and chemical hazards in the environment. Biological factors lead to infectious diseases. Although many of these diseases have proven difficult to eradicate, enough is known about them to identify actions that will drastically reduce their incidence. Chemical hazards in the environment can cause immediate, dangerous health effects and can also contribute to chronic, or long-term, problems. In contrast to infectious diseases, our understanding of how chemical exposures influence health, especially very low-level exposures typically found in the environment, remains incomplete.

BIOLOGICAL HAZARDS

Of all the environmental hazards humans encounter, the most formidable adversaries remain the microorganisms — viruses, bacteria, protozoa, and helminths. Up to 17 million deaths per year are attributable to these infectious and parasitic agents, almost all in the developing world, along with hundreds of millions of cases of sickness. Indeed, the history of humankind has been a struggle between humans and microbes. Years of concerted efforts have revealed that while it is very difficult to eradicate microbial threats, it is possible to live in balance with them. However, human activities that change the environment and disrupt natural ecosystems can tip the scales in favor of the microbes.

Why consider infectious diseases "environmental" in origin? Because most, though certainly not all, are intimately connected with conditions in the physical environment. Cholera and other diarrheal diseases, for instance, are associated with inadequate access to clean water and sanitation and poor hygiene. Intestinal worms, which debilitate hundreds of millions at any given time, are associated with contaminated or undercooked food — which in turn arise from inadequate water supplies and improper food preparation or storage.

Malaria, schistosomiasis, and other vector-borne diseases require certain ecological conditions for the vector — mosquito, fly, or snail — to persist. Environmental conditions increase the biological organisms' ability to thrive or spread. Although some supporting conditions exist in the natural environment, many are created or enhanced by human activities. Other diseases, such as acute respiratory infections or tuberculosis or measles, are linked with poor conditions within the household environment, including overcrowding, soot and smoke, and air pollution. The role of environmental factors here seems to be to weaken the body's natural defenses to organisms that are often present.

The agents that cause infectious disease require not only favorable environmental conditions but also a susceptible host. The most vulnerable people tend to be those with low or reduced immunity, such as those weakened by malnutrition or other infections. Children are particularly vulnerable, especially infants who are not breast-fed and thus do not have the advantage of the mother's immunity. For some infectious diseases, new migrants to an area are also at heightened risk because they have not been previously exposed to diseases endemic in the area and thus have not built up any defenses against them. The next section reviews the major infectious diseases and the environmental conditions that influence their incidence.

Water-, Food-, and Soilborne Diseases

Of all the infectious diseases, diarrhea has perhaps the clearest links to the environment and some of the most deadly repercussions. Diarrhea is spread by both bacteria and viruses through contaminated food or water, and these disease-causing agents represent one of the most widespread health problems in the contemporary world. Diarrhea killed roughly 2.5 million people in 1996, according to WHO, most of whom were children under age 5. In 1990, diarrhea accounted for 8 percent of DALYs globally. Diarrhea kills through dehydration. Fortunately, it is easily and fairly inexpensively managed with oral rehydration therapy (ORT), for those who have access to adequate medical care. Despite concerted efforts to make ORT widely available, the huge death toll from diarrhea clearly shows that much more remains to be done. Short of death, the roughly 4 billion episodes of diarrhea each year cause widespread debilitation.

Diarrhea is intimately connected to malnutrition, which increases the frequency and severity of diarrheal episodes; repeated bouts of diarrhea, in turn, exacerbate malnutrition. Among causative agents, one of the most common is the intestinal bacteria *E. coli*, although a variety of other pathogens can cause diarrhea. Diarrheal diseases arise through contact with feces and are spread by what is known as the fecal-oral route. Until recently, contaminated water supplies were thought to be the chief culprit, but now the pathway is known to be more complex.

An even greater factor appears to be insufficient water for washing, especially hand-washing, which makes proper hygiene impossible. When inadequate water supplies are coupled with shared latrines — or none at all — it creates conditions rife for transmitting diarrhea. Today, an estimated 2.9 billion people lack access to adequate sanitation and roughly 1.4 billion people do not have access to safe drinking water. This situation has persisted despite investments of more than US$100 billion during the International Water and Sanitation Decade.

Diarrheal diseases arise through contact with feces and are spread by what is known as the fecal-oral route. Until recently, contaminated water supplies were thought to be the chief culprit, but now the pathway is known to be more complex. An even greater factor appears to be insufficient water for washing, especially hand-washing, which makes proper hygiene impossible. When inadequate water supplies are coupled with shared latrines—or none at all—it creates conditions rife for transmitting diarrhea.

Today, an estimated 2.9 billion people lack access to adequate sanitation and roughly 1.4 billion people do not have access to safe drinking water. This situation has persisted despite investments of more than US$100 billion during the International Water and Sanitation Decade Improvements in coverage continue to be overtaken by rapid population growth and even more explosive urban growth. Ensuring access to adequate supplies of good-quality water and some form of sanitation — coupled with hygiene education and general socioeconomic development — remain critical factors in reducing the toll of diarrheal diseases.

Diarrheal diseases are by no means limited to the developing world, although they are most deadly there. In the developed world, where diarrhea is a major cause of sickness but rarely death, *Salmonella* and *Campylobacter jejuni*, spread through tainted chicken or milk, are among the most common agents. In addition, new microbial agents are increasingly implicated in human disease. *Campylobacter jejuni*, for instance, was once found only in animals, but now it is among the most common causes of foodborne illness in humans.

Public health officials in the United States and elsewhere warn of an epidemic of foodborne pathogens. Several recent outbreaks of food poisoning in the United States, Canada, Europe, and Japan have been linked with *Cyclospora* and a new, particularly vicious form of *E. coli*. To avert any possibility of a considerable outbreak, such as occurred in Japan in 1996 from *E. coli* O157, the U.S. Government in 1997 recalled more than 11 million kilograms of beef suspected to be contaminated with the organism.

In 1993, the United States experienced the largest outbreak of diarrhea in recent history — affecting more than 400,000 people — when the municipal water supply of Milwaukee, Wisconsin, was contaminated by *Cryptosporidium parvum* from farm animal wastes. This protozoan parasite has been wreaking havoc in countries across Europe as well, raising new concerns about the safety of drinking water in some of the world's most affluent countries. Other familiar and dangerous infectious diseases, such as cholera and hepatitis A and E, can also be transmitted by fecally contaminated food and water. This is most common in developing countries, but frequently occurs elsewhere. In the United States, for instance, 151 students and staff in four different school districts in Michigan developed hepatitis A in March 1997.

The cases have been associated with the consumption of frozen strawberries imported from Mexico. Cholera sweeps around the globe periodically in major pandemics. Annual death rates fluctuate wildly, ranging in recent years from several thousand up to hundreds of thousands. Most deaths occur in Africa, often among displaced or refugee populations; overall, some 79 million people in Africa alone are at risk for the disease, according to WHO.

Recent outbreaks in Latin America and the appearance of a new strain of cholera in India and Bangladesh provide examples of how changing environmental conditions can accelerate disease transmission. Among the food-, water-, and soilborne diseases, those caused by parasitic worms are noted for the debilitation they cause. At any one time, roughly 3.5 billion people are infected with one or several species of parasitic worms — making these among the most prevalent human infections — and some 450 million people are ill as a result. The chief transmission route is the familiar trail through human feces, via either contaminated food or soil. When an infected person defecates in the open, the soil becomes a breeding ground.

The contaminated soil is then carried into homes on the soles .of the feet. Not surprisingly, worm infections are on the rise in urban slums and shanty towns of the developing world, according to WHO. Rarely fatal, worm infections nonetheless exact a tremendous and diverse toll. Infection takes place repeatedly, and the disease becomes more serious as the worm burden in the body builds up. The most vulnerable group is school-aged children, who may harbor multiple infections simultaneously. The effects on children are especially pernicious because chronic infections impair both physical and intellectual growth and development.

The worm infection that is most deadly is schistosomiasis; it kills some 20,000 people a year and causes chronic ill health among hundreds of millions more. Safe and effective drugs cost 30 cents to treat one patient, but this cost is prohibitive in many countries.

The disease is caused by parasitic flatworms, called flukes, of the genus *Schistosoma*, whose intermediate hosts are snails common throughout Asia, Africa, and other tropical regions. These snails flourish in relatively calm supplies of fresh water WHO estimates that about 200 million people in tropical countries have acquired the disease from bathing or wading in infested rivers, lakes, and irrigation systems, and as many as 500 million to 600 million more are at risk.

Schistosomiasis is on the upswing in developing countries, in part because it spreads to previously unaffected areas through water development projects, such as dams or irrigation. As with diarrhea, providing for the sanitary disposal of feces would do much to prevent the transmission of schistosomiasis and other worm infections. The gains from improved sanitation may take years to materialize, however; in the near term, experts recommend a combined strategy that includes snail control, sanitary improvements, education, and repeated treatment with medicines to keep the worm burden low.

Insect-Borne Diseases

Malaria is the most deadly of the insect-borne diseases, claiming the lives of some 1 million to 3 million people each year — 90 percent of them in Africa, and most of them children. World Helath Organisation (WHO) estimates that some 300 million to 500 million cases of malaria occur each year — and the number is on the rise — and that 40 percent of the world's population is at risk for malaria. Malaria has been called the "laziness" disease because it is so debilitating.

The most prevalent disease in poor rural regions, malaria produces recurrent infections with attacks of fever in warm and rainy seasons, just when workers are needed to collect crops. Caused by four different species of protozoal parasites, malaria is transmitted through the bite of the *Anopheles* mosquito, which harbors the parasites. Thus, the geographic range of the disease is determined by the environmental conditions that the mosquito in question requires—a particular combination of altitude, rainfall, heat, and humidity, and available surface water. Because ideal conditions vary for the 60 or so species of *Anopheles* that transmit the disease, strategies designed to control one vector won't necessarily work for another.

In the tropics, where malaria is most entrenched and deadly, spread of the disease is abetted by conditions of heat, humidity, poverty, and inadequate waste disposal. Malaria is a particular problem in newly cultivated or frontier areas such as Amazonia- and areas of recent agricultural expansion. Once targeted for global eradication, malaria has turned out to be more than a worthy adversary. A more realistic goal is simply to control the disease. WHO has declared the mosquito "Public Enemy Number One" because it is involved in so many deadly or debilitating diseases — not just malaria but also dengue fever, yellow fever, filariasis (elephantiasis), and Japanese encephalitis. These diseases, too, are exquisitely attuned to changing environmental conditions. The *Aedes aegypti* mosquitoes that carry dengue and yellow fever, for instance, thrive in urban settings, where they lay their eggs in water storage containers or in discarded plastic bottles or tires.

In other vector-borne diseases, flies and other insects transmit the infectious parasite. Sleeping sickness (African trypanosomiasis) for instance, is transmitted by the bite of the tsetse fly. Leishmaniasis is transmitted by the sandfly, again through a parasite-contaminated bite. This disease is a major problem in parts of Africa, Latin America, and the Middle East, where some 2 million cases occur each year. In its deadliest form, visceral leishmaniasis, fatality rates can reach 100 percent if untreated.

In its more common form, the disease produces painful ulcers on the face, arms, and legs. WHO estimates that some 350 million people are at risk of contracting the leishmaniasis. As with other vector-borne diseases, its spread is accelerated by development projects such as road building or forest exploitation, which bring people into contact with the disease vector.

Leishmaniasis is reappearing in some areas where it had once been controlled, in part because of the cessation of insecticide spraying to control malaria. A beneficial side effect of DDT, it turns out, was that it kept sandflies in check. Chagas disease, also known as American trypanosomiasis, is unique to the Americas, where housing conditions pose the biggest risk factor. In this case the culprit, the parasite *T. cruzi*, is carried by both wild and domesticated animals. It is usually transmitted, however, by a blood-sucking bug that lives in thatched roofs.

About one third of those infected develop a chronic form of the disease, which can lead to heart damage and death. WHO estimates that Chagas disease is the leading cause of cardiac death among young adults in parts of South America.

Airborne Diseases

Commonly known as ARI, acute respiratory infections kill more than 4 million people per year and are the leading cause of death among children under age 5. This range of infections, which includes pneumonia in its most serious form, accounts for more than 8 percent of the global burden of disease. ARI's reach is global: it is the most frequent disease worldwide and a common causes of visits to pediatricians in the industrialized countries, although essentially all deaths from ARI occur in the developing world.

The risk factors for ARI are numerous and difficult to sort out. Caused by different viruses or bacteria, ARI is closely associated with poverty. Overcrowding and unsanitary household conditions favor the transmission of the disease, which is spread by droplets from a cough or a sneeze or unwashed hands. Death most often strikes those children who are already weakened by low birth weight, other infections, and malnutrition.

Several other factors seem to exacerbate the disease. Exposure to tobacco smoke increases the risk of contracting these infections, and many studies implicate both indoor and outdoor air pollution. Indoor air pollution has been the focus of particular concern, specifically, the soot and smoke associated with the burning of biomass fuels such as wood, coal, or dung. Many people in the developing world, mostly in rural areas, rely on biomass fuels for heating or cooking. A cause-and-effect relationship between indoor air pollution and ARI has been difficult to prove, however, in part because people who use biomass fuels tend to be poor and exposed to multiple risks such as overcrowding, tobacco smoke, and malnutrition. Even so, the World Bank estimated in 1992 that switching to better fuels could halve the number of pneumonia deaths.

Other airborne diseases also thrive in conditions of poverty, exploiting enclosed spaces, crowding, and poor hygienic conditions. Tuberculosis (TB), to name just one, killed an estimated 3 million people in 1996, and nearly 7.5 million others developed the disease. TB is the single largest cause of adult death from infectious diseases.

Roughly 95 percent of all TB sufferers are in the developing world, mostly in Southeast Asia, Western Pacific, and Africa — many in the slums of poor cities. In recent years, however, TB has resurfaced in developed countries, where it is concentrated among poor populations. Measles and diphtheria, also diseases of crowding and poverty, have been all but eliminated in the developed world since the advent of successful vaccines. In the developing world, however, measles still affects 42 million children per year who lack access to the vaccine; roughly 1 million of these children die. Since 1990, diphtheria has resurfaced in the former Soviet Union, triggered by social disruption and a drop in immunization rates.

Measles and diphtheria are just two of a cluster known as childhood (or vaccine-preventable) diseases. Other familiar diseases in this group are neonatal tetanus, poliomyelitis, and pertussis. This cluster, all linked with environmental conditions, accounts for nearly 15 percent of the total disease burden globally for children under age 5. Despite widespread immunization programs, these diseases nonetheless claimed the lives of 1,985,000 children in 1990.

CHEMICAL HAZARDS

Exposure to chemical agents in the environment — in air, water, food, and soil — has been implicated in numerous adverse effects, from cancer to lung disease to brain damage to birth defects. Some evidence is ironclad; some is suggestive at best. Although the acute effects such as poisonings are the best understood, it seems clear that hazardous pollutants contribute to the large and growing toll of chronic conditions, such as cancers and heart disease.

Chemical pollutants can also play a role in infectious diseases, perhaps by rendering the body less able to ward off infections. The exact magnitude of the risk they pose, however, is difficult to quantify. This has fueled an intense debate over what constitutes safe use and disposal of toxic substances. This debate has occurred mostly in the affluent countries but is increasingly occurring in the developing world as well. Although cause-and-effect relationships for most infectious diseases are well known, the links between chemical pollutants and disease are murkier.

A person contracting cholera, for instance, clearly has been exposed to the *cholera vibrio*. The circumstances of that exposure may remain mysterious — and other contributing factors may be involved — but exposure to the bacterium is an established causal factor. The same pathway cannot be traced for a disease such as lung cancer Cancers may take 10 to 40 years to develop, and many factors may contribute to the appearance of the disease in a particular person. Accordingly, chemical risks tend to be described in terms of the numbers of people exposed — for instance, 1.4 billion urban dwellers exposed to air quality that exceeds health guidelines, as WHO estimates. Such estimates reveal little about how many people will actually suffer the adverse effects from these exposures.

On a global scale, the health risk from chemical agents in the environment is considerably smaller than that from biological pathogens described in the previous section. In some heavily polluted areas, however, chemical risks can be quite high. Risks are likely to be higher in less developed as opposed to more developed countries, because fewer safeguards are typically in place there, either to reduce emissions or to protect people from exposure. Equally important, regardless of their magnitude, the risks from chemical pollutants are preventable.

Body of evidence

Environmental pollutants arise from many sources, and exposures may occur through many different routes. Many occur on the job, where workers are exposed to doses typically much higher than those encountered in the ambient environment. Although occupational exposures are a major source of ill health globally, this subject is outside the purview of this section, which focuses on chemicals in the ambient environment. Some pollutants of particular concern are airborne substances — primarily suspended particulates, sulfur dioxide, nitrogen oxides, ozone, and carbon monoxide — emitted as byproducts of energy production, industry, and transportation.

While most scientific attention and policy debate has focused on outdoor air pollutants, indoor air pollutants such as smoke and soot, arising from the burning of biomass fuels such as dung and wood, appear to pose an even greater risk to human health, because indoor exposures tend to be many times higher than those encountered outdoors. Hundreds of millions of people in the developing world are regularly exposed to potentially harmful indoor emissions, which are believed to contribute to chronic lung disease, cancer, and ARI.

Exposure to pesticides can occur directly, typically to agricultural workers and their families and those who live near farms where pesticides are heavily used. Exposures can also be indirect, when pesticides contaminate surface waters or groundwater or soil, or when pesticide residues on food or contaminated fish or wildlife are ingested. Some of the most problematic pesticides are organic compounds that are slow to degrade and thus persist in the environment for years, accumulating in animal and human tissues Some industrial chemicals, such as PCBs, also persist in the environment and have caused widespread environmental contamination. Exposure to industrial chemicals can result from intentional releases to either air or water, from accidents, or from the leaching of these substances from disposal sites into surrounding soil or water.

Heavy metals are used for a variety of agricultural and industrial purposes and are frequent contaminants in industrial wastes. Many are toxic: mercury, for instance, is a known neurotoxin; arsenic can cause skin and other cancers. One of the most important environmental pollutants is lead, which at even very low doses can cause significant neurological impairment and loss of intelligence.

Major sources of lead in the environment include exhaust from vehicles using leaded gasoline, lead-based paints, and some types of water pipes. Not surprisingly, much evidence of the harmful effects of industrial chemicals has come from the workplace, where exposures tend to be high and sustained relative to those in the ambient environment. For instance, studies of British textile workers alerted researchers to the link between asbestos and lung cancer. The reproductive toxicity of the pesticide DBCP (1, 2-dibromo-3-chloropropane) became startlingly clear in the late 1970s and early 1980s when male farm workers in the banana-growing region of Costa Rica were found to be sterile. By the mid-1990s, some 1,500 male workers had been medically diagnosed with sterility from exposure to DBCP. While these examples illuminate the risks of high-level exposures, they do not indicate the extent of risk posed by lower levels of exposures that are typically encountered in the environment.

One difficulty in determining the exact magnitude of the potential health risk is that epidemiologic studies, which look at differences between exposed and nonexposed groups, generally show a statistical association between an environmental exposure and adverse effects. They do not attempt to demonstrate cause and effect. In many cases, studies cannot reveal links between an exposure and an adverse effect unless the particular risk is quite high or the effect is unusual, as was the case with vinyl chloride and angiosarcoma, a relatively rare form of liver cancer. Given these difficulties, some studies will find an association, others will refute it. Thus, proof of a causal relationship often takes years to amass — as with smoking and lung cancer — if it is ever established. Calculating how much of a specific pollutant a person is exposed to can be daunting. For example, to assess air quality, a city might have only a few monitors dispersed throughout a wide geographic area.

The direction of the wind on any given day will do much to determine who is exposed, as will whether that person spent most of the day indoors or out. In addition, air pollution monitors are usually installed on rooftops, so recorded pollutant levels do not describe the exposure of a commuter stuck in traffic, or, say, a small child on a playground. So, although it is widely agreed that ambient air pollution at levels normally encountered in many cities can damage health and even kill, the magnitude of the effect remains controversial. In the absence of definitive human data, investigators often must rely on animal studies and quantitative risk assessment models to estimate the toxicity of a particular substance.

In some instances, health effects in wildlife have first alerted researchers to potential dangers of a class of environmental pollutants. For example, reproductive damages in seagulls and other wildlife presented some of the first clues about the adverse effects of DDT. More recently, reproductive anomalies in wildlife have sparked concern about the ability of some chemicals to cause ill effects by disrupting the body's normal hormonal system. Translating effects in wildlife to risks in humans, however, remains difficult. Even laboratory experiments in animals are less than definitive, because it is difficult to extrapolate from effects seen when high doses are given to animals to probable results from the low doses common to human exposure.

Despite widespread public concern over chemical safety, toxicity testing remains inadequate. For the vast majority of chemicals in widespread use, no toxicity testing results are available in the public record. Most of the testing for chronic effects that has occurred has focused on cancer. To date, about 74 chemicals or mixtures have been found to cause cancer in humans. Hundreds of others, however, cause cancer or mutations in cells or in animals, which raises concerns about their effects in humans. Of the other potential effects of chemical hazards, such as infertility, birth defects, immune system impairment, or brain damage, even less is known. In the United States, for instance, the chief agency for chemical evaluation spent nearly US$29 million on testing chemicals for cancer in 1991, but just about $6 million for both genetic and reproductive effects. Testing for other health concerns, such as immune system effects or endocrine disruption, lags even further behind.

Again, the United States provides an apt example: according to a recent study, 86 percent of chemicals in widespread use have not been tested for immunotoxicity, and 67 percent have not been tested for neurotoxicity. This focus on cancer means that other important and preventable risks may be overlooked. Standard methods of toxicity testing, for instance, would not have identified lead as a significant hazard — even though the U.S. Centers for Disease Control and Prevention has called lead poisoning the single, most significant preventable disease associated with environmental and occupational exposures. More precise techniques to evaluate chemical safety are under development, including mechanistic studies to illuminate exactly what changes a chemical exerts within a cell. Such methods, however, tend to be time-consuming and expensive and thus are not widely applicable in large-scale studies.

Meanwhile, policymakers must rely on the best available data — often from animal studies and risk assessments — in setting policies to protect the public from suspected risks. Because chemical products are so widely used and evidence suggests they may damage the environment and human health, governments face increasing pressure to adopt the "precautionary principle." This principle affirms that when harm is strongly suspected, it is best to take action to prevent exposure, even if absolute proof of harm is missing.

Such prudent policies are by no means the norm. As described in more detail in many chemicals banned in developed countries are still in widespread use throughout the developing world, despite their known hazards, because they are cheap and effective. Among them is a class of particularly hazardous products known as persistent organic pollutants (POPs). Similarly, roughly two decades after the United States began to phase out the use of lead in gasoline because of its well-known health effects, it remains ubiquitous throughout much of Asia and Latin America.

Efforts to minimize pollutants' harmful impacts are complicated by the increasing realization that they can harm human health not just through direct toxicological routes but also indirectly, through large-scale ecological disruptions. This realization hit home with the unexpected discovery in 1985 of a "hole" in the stratospheric ozone layer, caused by human activity leading to chlorofluorocarbon emissions.

The health impacts of this thinning ozone layer, which protects the Earth from harmful ultraviolet radiation, range from skin cancer to cataracts to immune system depression to disruption of the food chain. None of these results was anticipated a mere 15 years ago. Similarly, the combustion of fossil fuels not only causes urban air pollution but also disrupts atmospheric chemistry and may lead to global warming. Plausible health impacts include increased deaths from excessive heat episodes and violent storms, and a greater toll from malaria and other vector-borne diseases in developing countries.

NATURAL HAZARDS

Within nature nothing is constant. Indeed, nature is typified by continual changes, in some cases by predictable evolution or the normal sequence of cyclical events as in seasonal weather. Much of nature, though, is unpredictable. When unpredictable natural events become extreme in their occurrence, they may constitute a danger to humans and to the other members of an environment. Such an event, then, defines a natural hazard. Another way of conceptualizing natural hazard is as the coexistence of people in a natural environment that may disrupt or threaten their safety, property, or livelihood at an unpredictable time.

There are many such natural events that, when experienced in an extreme degree, may become a risk to the inhabitants of an environment. These include avalanche, coastal erosion, drought, earthquake, flood, fog, frost, hail, landslide, lightning, snow, tornado, tropical cyclone, volcano, and wind. Some forms of environmental degradation may also contribute to the creation of hazards or be an extension of them, such as deforestation and desertification.

This course will focus on high priority/high incidence hazards in developing countries. These are hazards that governments or other agencies have targeted to reduce the social dislocations from catastrophes.

Another focus of the course will be to demonstrate the relationship between natural hazards and disasters. In fact, the hazard may be viewed as the triggering device for the disaster to occur. Often times the disaster is brought on by the mere presence of human settlement in an area that perhaps should not be occupied, as in flood plains. Or the impact of human intervention in natural processes may trigger a disaster, as in a flash flood in a deforested area.

Why are natural hazards such a universal concern? The disasters they cause kill and injure people worldwide. They cause emotional stress and trauma. They destroy homes and businesses, damage agriculture and disrupt both local and national economies. And disasters are increasing, both in number and in people affected. The disasters that have increased during the past decade include floods, storms, earthquakes, tsunamis, and droughts. Only in less important categories such as epidemics, avalanches and fires has there been some decrease.

The average number of disasters per year was greater in the 1970s than in the 1960s. Many more people died per year in disasters in the 1970s than in the 1960s. The difference is far too great to be explained by statistical bias or population growth alone. Figures for the number of people affected per year also increased: 27.7 million in the 1960s and 48.3 million in the 1970s, according to the Swedish Red Cross report.

— Drought led the list, affecting 24.4 million a year in the 1970s up from 18.5 million the previous decade.

— But floods showed the steepest rise, from 5.2 million in the 1960s to 15.4 million in the 1970s.

If the number of "people affected" actually included the people who pay tax or otherwise contribute to the disaster response, then the number of people affected would be far greater. Not included in the above statistics is the growing threat from technological hazards such as liquid nitrogen gas, cyanide, nuclear reactors, etc. Nor is the disaster created by civil strife treated here. A discussion of these dangers is beyond the scope of this course.

What are disasters?

Natural hazards such as earthquakes, hurricanes, floods, and droughts spring to mind when the word "disaster" is mentioned. But a disaster should be defined on the basis of its human consequences, not on the phenomenon that caused it. An earthquake is simply an event in nature. Even a very strong one is not a disaster unless it causes injury or destroys property. Thus an earthquake occurring in an uninhabited area is only of scientific interest and is not considered a disaster.

When a natural event does affect a human settlement, the result may still not be a major disaster. Consider the earthquake that struck San Fernando, California, in 1971. The quake registered 6.4 on the Richter scale, yet the region around

San Fernando Valley suffered only minor damage and 58 deaths. Two years later, though, an earthquake of a magnitude of 6.2 struck Managua, Nicaragua, and reduced the center of the city to rubble, killing an estimated 6,000 people. A disaster can be more precisely defined as an occurrence of widespread severe damage, injury, or loss of life or property with which a community cannot cope and during which the society undergoes severe disruption.

While some developed nations may be as prone to disasters as poor nations, the people of wealthier nations are not as vulnerable to disasters; they do not die in as large numbers nor does their environment collapse as easily. Both Tokyo, Japan, and Managua, Nicaragua, are prone to earthquakes. But the people of Tokyo are far less vulnerable to injury by .earthquake because Tokyo has strictly enforced building codes, zoning regulations and earthquake training and communications systems. In Managua, there are still many people living in top-heavy mud houses on hillsides. They are vulnerable.

This difference is shown by a list of disaster events and fatalities over 1960-81:

— Japan suffered 43 earthquakes and other disasters and lost 2,700 people: 63 deaths per disaster.

— Peru suffered 31 disasters with 91,000 dead, the vase majority lost in the single event of the 1970 earthquake.

Rapid population growth, urban migration, inequitable patterns of land ownership, lack of education, subsistence agriculture on marginal lands, etc. lead to vulnerable conditions such as unsafe siting of buildings and settlements, unsafe homes, malnutrition, unemployment and underemployment, illiteracy, etc. The poor within the poor countries are the most vulnerable. Landslides or flooding disasters are closely linked to rapid and unchecked urbanization that forces low-income families to settle on the slopes of steep hillsides or ravines, or along the banks of flood-prone rivers. Famines can be closely linked to shortages of purchasing power caused by rural unemployment or a sudden influx of refugees into a country from a strife-torn neighboring country. High numbers of deaths accompanying earthquakes almost always result from structural collapse of poor, low-cost houses.

In other disasters, such as cyclones and tsunamis, humans can increase their vulnerability by removing bits of their natural environment that may act as buffers to these extreme natural forces. Such acts include destroying reefs, cutting natural wind breaks and clearing inland forests. The poor countries that suffer the worst disasters are the same countries in which environmental degradation is proceeding most rapidly. Countries with severe deforestation, erosion, overcultivation and overgrazing tend to be hardest hit by disasters.

Therefore, it can be said that nature causes extreme events (called "hazards" when they threaten people), but people create disasters by :

— making faulty assessments of natural hazard risks

— undermining the resilience of impacted natural and social systems, and

— failing to practice appropriate protective measures.

Natural hazards are agents or trigger mechanisms that can come into contact with a vulnerable human condition to result in a disaster.

Classifications of disasters

Hazards and the disasters they cause are classified as rapid onset or cataclysmic, and long-term or continuing. In a cataclysmic disaster, one large-scale event causes most of the damage and destruction. Following this event, there may be a tremendous amount of suffering and chaos, but things soon begin to improve. In a long-term, continuing disaster, the situation after the event remains constant or may even deteriorate as time passes. Cataclysmic disasters include earthquakes, volcanic eruptions, cyclonic storms, and floods. Continuing natural disasters include droughts, crop failures, and environmental degradation such as deforestation and desertification. The damaged area in a cataclysmic disaster is usually relatively small, while the area affected in a continuing disaster may be extremely large.

Cataclysmic disasters destroy buildings and entire human settlements. Loss of life is sudden and therefore dramatic. In terms of food and food distribution, cataclysmic disasters are normally more disruptive than destructive. For example, they may disrupt the transport and marketing systems. They can disrupt or damage irrigation systems and, to a limited extent, they may destroy food supplies. But the extent of destruction depends on the season, the location of the disaster, and the total area affected. On the other hand, while continuing disasters disrupt transportation and distribution networks, they can also bring them to a complete halt and ultimately destroy the system itself.

Phases of a disaster

Disaster specialists have consistently made efforts to classify the time periods of a disaster. Among the standard classifications used are: the pre-disaster periods, the warning phase, the emergency phase, the rehabilitation phase, the recovery phase, and the reconstruction phase. The length of time any one period will last can vary greatly depending on the type of disaster and other factors. People involved in disasters must recognize the different phases and the appropriate activities that occur in each phase. It is difficult to set time limits on the post-disaster time phases or to accurately define the limits of each, even for one specific type of disaster. For example, the emergency phase of a hurricane or a flood may be only a few days, or as long as a week. A volcano may precipitate an emergency period of only a few days or up to a month and may cause immediate danger to the area for years. An earthquake may have continuing aftershocks after the first major tremor, thus prolonging the emergency for a number of weeks. This was the case in China in 1976. A drought and a resulting famine can last for months or even a year or more. And of course wars and the refugee crises they can initiate may last for many years.

Pre-disaster activities

These activities are normally subdivided into disaster prevention, disaster mitigation and disaster preparedness. In general, disaster prevention is event-focused. In other words, the objective of prevention is to prevent the disaster from occurring at all. Disaster mitigation accepts the fact that some natural event may occur but tries to lessen the impact by improving the community's ability to absorb the impact with little damage or disruptive effects. Disaster preparedness assumes that the disaster will occur and focuses on structuring response and laying a framework for recovery.

Emergency response activities are those carried out during the actual emergency or immediately prior to it. This may involve evacuation of threatened communities, emergency assistance during the disaster, and actions taken in the immediate aftermath during the time when the community is rather disorganized and basic services and infrastructure are not fully functioning. Because the emergency period is both dramatic and traumatic, most attention by the press and international community is focused here. Yet in most disasters, the emergency passes rather quickly and, in reality, only accounts for a very small percentage of the total picture.

Post-disaster recovery can be subdivided into two phases. The first begins at the end of the emergency phase. It is a transitional phase when people and community systems try to reestablish a semblance of normalcy. This period is usually characterized by such activities as business reopening in damaged structures, farmers returning to reclaim and clear their land, and resumption of basic infrastructure services such as water and sanitation systems in urban areas. The reconstruction phase is marked by large-scale efforts to replace damaged buildings, revitalize economies or restore agricultural systems to their full pre-disaster production capacity.

Effects of disasters

Each type of disaster can have a number of disruptive effects. These in turn cause generally predictable problems and needs of four kinds: environmental; health; social, economic, and political; and administrative and managerial.

Disasters can have any number or combination of four effects: destruction and damage to homes and buildings; decreased quantity or quality of water supplies; destruction of crops and or food stocks; and the presence of unburied human bodies or animal carcasses. These environmental effects vary considerably from disaster to disaster. For example, earthquakes affect buildings but usually not crops, while tropical cyclones may affect both. Closely related to the environmental effects is the impact that disasters have on land tenure and values. These effects also vary with the disaster type; for example, land values after earthquakes will go up in zones that were not heavily damaged, but land values go down in zones of active volcanoes.

Sudden natural disasters are often believed to cause not only widespread death but also massive social disruption and outbreaks of epidemic disease and famine, leaving survivors entirely dependent on outside relief. Systematic observation of the effects of disaster on human health has led to rather different conclusions, both about the effects of disaster on health and about the most effective ways of providing relief. Though all disasters are unique in that they affect areas with differing social, medical, and economic backgrounds, there are still similarities between disasters that, if recognized, can optimize the management of health relief and use of resources. The following points may be noted:

— There is a relationship between the type of disaster and its effect on health. This is particularly true of the immediate impact in causing injuries: earthquakes regularly cause many injuries requiring medical care, while floods, storm surges and seismic sea waves cause relatively few.

— Some effects are a potential rather than an inevitable threat to health. For example, population movement and other environmental changes may lead to increased risk of disease transmission, although epidemics generally do not result from disasters.

— The actual and potential health risks after disaster do not all occur at the same time. Instead, they tend to arise at different times and to vary in importance within a disaster-affected area. Thus, casualties occur mainly at the time and place of impact and require immediate medical care. The risks of increased disease transmission take longer to develop and are greatest where there is crowding and reduced standards of sanitation.

— Disaster-created needs for food, shelter, and primary health care are usually not total. Even displaced persons often salvage some of the basic necessities of life. Further, people generally recover quickly from their immediate shock and spontaneously engage in search and rescue, transport of the injured, and other private relief activities.

Economic, social, and political effects

Disasters disrupt rather than destroy economies. During an emergency, people must leave their jobs and devote their time to disaster-related activities, such as search and rescue, or to care of survivors. During this period normal economic activities are severely curtailed, even if the sources of employment are unaffected by the disaster. This period is short-lived, however, and in the later phases of a disaster economic activities quickly assume a high priority for both businesses and victims alike. Whether or not an economy can recover quickly depends on the losses sustained. Physical damage to businesses and industry may temporarily halt some activities, but most enterprises can operate at reduced levels even with the loss of equipment. Often the workers in a damaged factory can be put to work helping to repair or rebuild the facility. In any case, the loss of jobs is usually only temporary.

Of far more concern is the impact of disasters on persons who are participating only marginally in the economy, people such as subsistence farmers, small shopkeepers, and fishermen. After a disaster it is not uncommon for many small enterprises to fail. For the owners, a disaster can wipe out not only their investments but also their savings. Several observers have noted that boom economies often develop after a widespread disaster such as an earthquake or hurricane requiring major physical reconstruction. Long-term effects are not yet known, but at least one study indicates that if low- income victims are given priority in job hiring, boom economies can be a means of adjusting some of the losses.

Administrative and managerial effects

Administrative problems in disaster are made more difficult by four factors, which increase in importance with the extent of the disaster.

1. *Effects on community leadership:* The loss of leaders due to death or injury can impair disaster response.
2. *Disruption of formal organizations:* When a disaster strikes, large formal organizations are most disrupted. Small, community- based organizations are generally better able to function, even with loss of leaders.
3. *Damage to critical facilities and lifelines:* Widespread disasters can destroy or damage facilities that may be critical

not only for responding to the disaster but also for maintaining a safe environment and public order. Among these are communications installations; electrical generating and transmission facilities; water storage, purification, and pumping facilities; sewage treatment facilities; hospitals; police stations; and other private buildings

4. *Disruption of transportation:* During the initial stages of most types of disasters, almost all surface means of transportation within a community are disrupted. Bridges can be knocked out; roads can be cut by landslides; rubble can block streets and highways.

PREVENTION, MITIGATION AND PREPAREDNESS

Up until this point, disasters have been discussed in terms of reaction, both by the affected societies and the relief agencies. An underlying theme, however, has been that disasters are not unforeseen events. The technology now exists to identify the hazards that threaten a community and to estimate the areas and the settlements that will be affected. One can then take steps to prevent the disaster, or prepare for the disaster and substantially reduce, or mitigate, its impact. These actions are known as pre-disaster planning.

Frederick Krimgold pioneered the early conceptualization of pre- disaster planning, which he describes as follows:

— Planning may be defined as the process of preparing a set of decisions for action in the future directed at achieving goals by optimal means. The stated goals of disaster relief are the reduction of human suffering, the improvement of material well- being, and the increase of personal security. It goes without saying that these goals are best served if disaster, in the first place, can be avoided or reduced. Thus, the primary goal of pre- disaster planning may be seen as the prevention or mitigation of disaster. If we refer to the definition of disaster in terms of the need for outside help, we may describe the goal of pre- disaster planning as the creation of self-sufficiency in dealing with natural phenomena. In those cases where prevention is not possible, the goal must be to plan for the effective application of aid.

Disaster prevention and mitigation should be in the forefront of the reader's mind throughout this course. Indeed, all disaster managers, whether full-time professionals or part-time volunteers, are challenged to accept disaster prevention and mitigation not only as a role to play but as their responsibility to their society, constituency, or clientele. One of the primary objectives of this course is for its students to become advocates for programs in disaster prevention, mitigation or improvements in the disaster response system.

Individuals working within government will have opportunities to increase their country's safety by promoting several activities. The most appropriate activity will obviously depend on their position in government. By the end of this course, each individual will no doubt be able to identify opportunities for personal and official involvement. For example, a person within a ministry devoted to natural resource development will see the need to conduct hazard mapping of seismic risk areas, flood prone areas, and perhaps zones subject to landslides. An employee within a ministry in charge of communication will see the need to integrate a complete disaster warning system with the national communication networks and to develop guidelines on communicating disaster emergencies to the central government and the public.

An official of a national bank will become aware of the need to include disaster mitigation measures and also criteria for the financing of projects that take into account disaster risks.

Non-government organizations including private voluntary organizations (volags) have other possible opportunities to implement improved disaster management programs. The traditional role of these groups is to react to disasters in the form of emergency relief and sometimes long-term recovery programs. As other courses offered by the Disaster Management Center will show, there are many areas where other professional and effective disaster response is achievable. It is also expected that the volags who are aware of disaster issues will support projects that improve a community's disaster risk awareness, promote economic or social development in ways that encourage disaster prevention or mitigation, and train their own staff and local individuals in disaster management.

The objectives for all participants in effective hazard management are many. Some, such as the reduction of loss of life, injury and property, have already been mentioned. Beyond those primary concerns are the related benefits of the maintenance of economic and social stability and the utilization of scarce resources for development instead of disaster recovery. The ultimate objective of this course, indeed the purpose of the Disaster Management Center at the University of Wisconsin, is to contribute to those objectives stated by Krimgold. An understanding of the nature of natural hazards is the first step in preparing for them. Being able to anticipate their consequences is a prerequisite not only to appropriate action following disaster events but also to prevention of them. The following lessons seek to provide an introduction to that process.

4

Green House Effect—An Impending Catastrophe

The "greenhouse effect" is the process by which an atmosphere warms a planet. Mars, Venus and other celestial bodies with atmospheres (such as Titan) have greenhouse effects, but for simplicity this chapter will refer to the case of Earth.

The term *greenhouse effect* may be used to refer to two different things in common parlance: the natural greenhouse effect, which refers to the greenhouse effect which occurs naturally on earth, and the enhanced (anthropogenic) greenhouse effect, which results from human activities. The former is accepted by all; the latter is a matter of some dispute.

NATURAL GREENHOUSE EFFECT

Process

The earth receives an enormous amount of solar radiation. Just above the atmosphere, the solar power flux density averages about 1367 watts/m^2, over the entire earth. This figure *vastly* exceeds the power generated by human activities.

The solar power hitting earth must be continually balanced by an equal amount of power radiating from the earth, or the earth's temperature would increase without limit. The radiation leaving the earth takes two forms: reflected solar radiation and thermal blackbody radiation.

Reflected solar radiation accounts for 30% of the earth's total radiation: on average, 6% of the incoming solar radiation is reflected by the atmosphere, 20% is reflected by clouds, and 4% is reflected by the surface.

The remaining 70% of the incoming solar radiation is absorbed: 16% by the atmosphere (including the almost complete absorption of shortwave UV over most areas by the stratospheric ozone layer); 3% by clouds; and 51% by the land and oceans. This absorbed energy heats the atmosphere, oceans and land.

Like the sun, the earth is a thermal blackbody radiator. But because the earth's surface is much cooler than the sun (287 K vs 5780 K), Wien's Displacement Law dictates that the earth must radiate its thermal energy at much longer wavelengths than the sun. While the sun's radiation peaks at a visible wavelength of 500 nanometers, earth's radiation peak is in the longwave (far) infrared at about 10 micrometres.

The earth's atmosphere is largely transparent at visible and near-infrared wavelengths, but not at 10 micrometres. Only about 6% of the earth's total radiation to space is direct thermal radiation from the surface. The atmosphere absorbs 71% of the surface thermal radiation before it can escape. The atmosphere itself behaves as a blackbody radiator in the far infrared, so it re-radiates this energy.

The earth's atmosphere and clouds therefore account for 91.4% of its longwave infrared radiation and 64% of the earth's total emissions at all wavelengths. The atmosphere and clouds get this energy from the solar energy they directly absorb; thermal radiation from the surface; and from heat brought up by convection and the condensation of water vapor.

Because the atmosphere is such a good absorber of longwave infrared, it effectively forms a one-way blanket over the earth's surface. Visible and near-visible radiation from the sun easily gets through, but thermal radiation from the surface can't easily get back out. In response, the earth's surface warms up. The power of the surface radiation increases by the Stefan-Boltzmann law until it compensates for the atmospheric absorption and a new equilibrium temperature is reached.

Any change to the earth's atmosphere that impedes or facilitates the transmission of longwave infrared radiation will upset this equilibrium, and the earth's surface will warm or cool until a new equilibrium temperature is reached.

The result of the greenhouse effect is that average surface temperatures are considerably higher than they would otherwise be if the earth's surface temperature were determined solely by the albedo and blackbody properties of the surface.

Limiting factors

The degree of the greenhouse effect is dependent primarily on the concentration of greenhouse gases in the planetary atmosphere. The carbon dioxide-rich atmosphere of Venus causes a *runaway greenhouse effect* with surface temperatures hot enough to melt lead, the atmosphere of Earth creates habitable temperatures, and the thin atmosphere of Mars causes a minimal greenhouse effect.

The use of the term *runaway* greenhouse effect to describe the effect as it occurs on Venus emphasises the interaction of the greenhouse effect with other processes in feedback cycles. Venus is sufficiently strongly heated by the Sun that water is vaporised and so carbon dioxide is not reabsorbed by the planetary crust. As a result, the greenhouse effect has been progressively intensified by positive feedback. On Earth there is a substantial hydrosphere and biosphere which respond to higher temperatures by recycling atmospheric carbon more quickly (in geologic terms; the timescale for the ocean/biosphere to remove a CO_2 perturbation is on the order of several hundred years). The presence of liquid water thus limits the increase in the greenhouse effect through negative feedback. This state of affairs is expected to persist for at least hundreds of millions of years, but, ultimately, the warming of an aging Sun will overwhelm this regulatory effect.

The greenhouse gases

Greenhouse gases are gaseous components of the atmosphere that contribute to the greenhouse effect. The major natural greenhouse gases are water vapor, which causes about 60% of the greenhouse effect on Earth, carbon dioxide (about 26%), and ozone.

Minor greenhouse gases include methane, nitrous oxide, sulfurhexafluoride (SF_6) and halocarbons such as perfluoromethane, freon and other CFCs.

The major atmospheric constituents (N_2 and O_2) are not greenhouse gases, because homonuclear diatomic molecules (eg N_2, O_2, H_2 ...) do not absorb in the infrared as there is no net change in the dipole moment of these molecules.

Real greenhouses

The term 'greenhouse effect' originally came from the greenhouses used for gardening, but it is a misnomer since greenhouses operate differently. A greenhouse is built of glass; it heats up primarily because the Sun warms the ground inside it, which warms the air near the ground, and this air is prevented from rising and flowing away. This can be demonstrated by opening a small window near the roof of a greenhouse: the temperature will drop considerably. It has also been demonstrated experimentally. Greenhouses thus work by preventing *convection*; the greenhouse effect however reduces *radiation loss*, not convection.

Effects of various gases

It is hard to disentangle the percentage contributions to the "GH" effect from different gases, because there are overlaps in the IR spectrum of the various gases. However, one can calculate the percentage of trapped radiation remaining, and discover:

Species removed	% trapped radiation remaining
All	0
H_2O, CO_2, O_3	50
H_2O	64
Clouds	86
CO_2	88
O_3	97
None	100

Water vapour effects

Water vapor is the major contributor to Earth's greenhouse effect. Its effects vary due to localized concentrations, mixture with other gases, frequencies of light, different behavior in different levels of the atmosphere, and whether positive or negative feedback takes place. High humidity also affects cloud formation, which has major effects upon temperature but is distinct from water vapor gas.

Water vapor (H_2O) causes about 60% of Earth's naturally-occurring greenhouse effect. Other gases influencing the effect include carbon dioxide (CO_2) (about 26%), methane (CH_4), nitrous oxide (N_2O) and ozone (O_3) (about 8%). Collectively, these gases are known as greenhouse gases.

The wavelengths of light that a gas absorbs can be modelled with quantum mechanics based on atomic properties of different gas molecules. It so happens that tri- (and more) atomic gases absorb strongly in infra-red wavelengths, which is why H_2O and CO_2 are greenhouses gases but the major atmospheric constituents (N_2 and O_2) are not.

The IPCC TAR reports that, despite non-uniform effects and difficulties in assessing the quality of the data, water vapour has generally increased over the 20th Century.

Estimates of the percentage of Earth's greenhouse effect due to water vapor:

— 36%

— 60-70% Nova.

Water vapour in the troposphere, unlike the better-known greenhouse gases such as CO_2, is essentially passive in terms of climate: the residence time for water vapour in the atmosphere is short (about a week) so perturbations to water vapour rapidly re-equilibriate. In contrast, the lifetimes of CO_2, methane, etc, are long (hundreds of years) and hence perturbations remain.

Thus, in response to a temperature perturbation caused by enhanced CO_2, water vapour would increase, resulting in a (limited) positive feedback and higher temperatures. In response to a perturbation from enhanced water vapour, the atmosphere would re-equilibriate due to clouds causing reflective cooling and water-removing rain. The contrails of high-flying aircraft sometimes form high clouds which seem to slightly alter the local weather.

Anthropogenic greenhouse gases

Human activity contributes to the greenhouse effect primarily by releasing carbon dioxide, but other gases, e.g. methane, are not negligible. The concentrations of several greenhouse gases have increased over time due to human activities, such as:

— burning of fossil fuels and deforestation leading to higher carbon dioxide concentrations,

— cattle and paddy rice farming, land use and wetland changes, and pipeline losses leading to higher methane concentrations,

— the use of CFCs in refrigeration and fire suppression systems.

According to the global warming hypothesis, greenhouse gases from industry and agriculture are partly or wholly to blame for recent global warming. Carbon dioxide is the subject of the proposed Kyoto Protocol. Nitrous oxide and methane are also taken into account in the international agreements, but not ozone. At least one IPCC TAR chapter lead author considers mention of the effect of water vapor upon the Earth's greenhouse effect to be misleading as water vapor can not be controlled by humans.

Increase of greenhouse gases

Since the beginning of the Industrial Revolution, the concentrations of many of the greenhouse gases have increased.

— As of 1994, Carbon dioxide is up 30%, from 278 ppvm to 358 ppvm; ten years later, the latest measurements from Mauna Loa show it to be at 379 ppvm

— Methane is up from 700 ppvb to 1721 ppvb

— Nitrous oxide 15%, from 275 to 311 ppvb

— CFC-12 from 0 to 0.503 ppvb

— HCFC-22 from 0 to 0.105 ppvb

— Perfluoromethane from 0 to 0.070 ppvb

— Sulphur hexafluoride from 0 to 0.032 ppvb

Duration of stay and global warming potential

The greenhouse gases, once in the atmosphere, do not remain there eternally. They can be withdrawn from the atmosphere:

— as a consequence of a physical phenomenon (rain, condensation, remove water vapor from the atmosphere)

— as a consequence of a chemical phenomenon intervening within the atmosphere. This is the case for methane, which is partly eliminated by reaction with radicals OH naturally present in the atmosphere, to give CO_2 (this effect due to the production of CO_2 is not included in the methane GWP)

— as a consequence of a chemical phenomenon intervening at the border between the atmosphere and the other compartments of the planet. This is the case for CO_2, which is reduced by photosynthesis of plants, and which is also dissolved in the ocean to end up giving bicarbonate and carbonate ions (CO_2 is chemically stable in the atmosphere)

— as a consequence of a radiative phenomenon. For example the electromagnetic radiation emitted by the sun and cosmic rays break molecular bonds of species in the upper atmosphere. Some halocarbons disappear in this way (they are generally too stable to disappear by chemical reaction in the atmosphere).

The lifetime of an individual molecule of gas in the atmosphere is frequently much shorter than the lifetime of a concentration anomaly of that gas. Thus, because of large (balanced) natural fluxes to and from the biosphere and ocean surface layer, an individual CO_2 molecule may last only a few years in the air, on average; however, the calculated lifetime of an increase in atmospheric CO_2 level is hundreds of years.

Aside from water vapour near the surface, which is has a residence time of few days, the greenhouse gases take a very long time to leave the atmosphere. It is not easy to know with precision how long is necessary, because the atmosphere is a very complex system. However, there are estimates of the duration of stay, i.e. the time which is necessary so that the gas disappears from the atmosphere, for the principal ones.

Duration of stay and warming capability of the different greenhouse gases can be compared:

— CO_2 duration stay is variable (approx 200-450 years) and its global warming potential (GWP) is defined as 1.

— Methane duration stay is of 12.2 +/- 3 years and a GWP of 22 (meaning that it has 22 times the warming ability of carbon dioxide),

— Nitrous oxide has a duration stay of 120 years and a GWP of 310

— CFC-12 has a duration stay of 102 years and a GWP between 6200 and 7100

— HCFC-22 has a duration stay of 12.1 years and a GWP between 1300 and 1400.

— Perfluoromethane has a duration stay of 50,000 years and a GWP of 6500

— Sulphur hexafluoride has a duration stay of 3 200 years and a GWP of 23900.

GLOBAL WARMING

Global warming is an increase over time of the average temperature of Earth's atmosphère and oceans. The global warming theory states that the temperature has risen since the late 19th century due to human causes, principally emissions of CO_2 increasing the "greenhouse effect". The theory further predicts that temperatures will continue to increase in the future, if human emissions of greenhouse gases continue.

Use of the term "global warming" generally implies a human influence — the more neutral term climate change is usually used for a change in climate with no presumption as to cause. Sometimes the term anthropogenic climate change is used to indicate the presumption of human influence.

Note that although the discussion often focusses on temperature, global warming or any climate change implies changes in other variables: overall precipitation and its patterns, cloud cover, weather, and all the other elements of our atmospheric system will be impacted by the increase in "radiative forcing" due to human changes in greenhouse gas concentrations in the atmosphere.

Possible explanations for observations of global warming are discussed in attribution of recent climate change.

The Kyoto Protocol proposes binding greenhouse gas limits for developed countries.

Scientific opinion

Since it is such an important issue, governments need predictions of future trends in global change so they can take political decisions to avoid undesired impacts. Global warming is being studied by the Intergovernmental Panel on Climate Change (IPCC). The IPCC does not commission or carry out research itself, but rather disseminates the body of published research. The reports reflect the consensus of the published science.

The 1995 IPCC report concluded that "The balance of evidence suggests a discernible human influence on global climate"; this was strengthened in the 2001 TAR to "There is new and stronger evidence that most of the warming observed over the last 50 years is attributable to human activities".

A survey in 1996 by Dennis Bray and Hans von Storch of the Meteorologisches Institut der Universitat Hamburg generated responses from over 400 German, American and Canadian climate researchers and was reported in the *United Nations Climate Change Bulletin*. The survey reported the response of scientists in this field, to the statement that it is "certain that, without change in human behavior, global warming will definitely occur sometime in the future". Scientists polled gave this statement an average score of 2.6 on a scale from 1 to 7, where 1 indicated complete agreement and 7 indicated complete disagreement.

Theories and criticisms

Leaving the realm of scientific journals, the debate has spilled out into the public arena, with some politicians making the issue a component of their campaigns for high office, such as Al Gore, author of *Earth in the Balance*. Global warming is a more central and sustained issue, however, for the EU.

Much about global warming theories is controversial, particularly whether there exists a scientific consensus sufficient to justify concerted international action to ameliorate its effects.

Proponents of global warming theory (GWT) express a wide range of opinions. Some merely recognize the validity of the observed increases in temperature. Others support measures such as the Kyoto Protocol that are intended to have some near-future climate effects and to lead eventually to further measures. Others believe that the environmental damage will have such severe impact that immediate steps must be taken to reduce CO_2 emissions, regardless of the economic costs to advanced nations such as the United States (the United States has the largest emissions of greenhouse gases of any country in absolute terms, and the second largest *per capita* emissions after Australia. There are no known climatologists supporting this viewpoint.

Critics of the global warming theory similarly offer a wide spectrum of opinions. Some, such as Patrick Michaels, propose that human influence has warmed the atmosphere yet dispute the conclusion of the IPCC TAR, which says "[t]here is new and stronger evidence that most of the warming observed over the last 50 years is attributable to human activities". Others conclude observations of global temperatures over much larger time spans, spans of thousands of years rather than decades – epochs rather than centuries, show global temperatures fluctuated wildly in the past long before the introduction of human industrial activity such as the industrial revolution. An additional assertion of many critics is that it cannot be possible to ascertain any definitive global temperature trend from the limited temperature record having often been cited — the Earth is much older than that, they affirm. Other scientists theorize global temperature change may in fact be induced by natural causes, such as volcanism and solar activity.

The above paragraphs might give the impression that belief in the course of past climate change correlates strongly with advocacy for future actions: this is not necessarily so. It is possible, perhaps common, to study the past record and give no counsel on the future.

Temperature records

The period of time over which the change has been observed may vary according to the focus of the user of the term: sometime since the Industrial Revolution, or since the beginning of an approximately global historical temperature record in about 1860; or over the past century; or the most recent 50 years.

10 centuries of NH temperature

Over the past 20,000 years the dominant temperature signal has been the end of the last ice age, approximately 12,000 years ago. Since then the temperature has been quite stable, though with various fluctuations, e.g. Medieval Warm Period or Little Ice Age. Over the past century or so the global (land + sea) temperature has increased by approximately 0.4–0.8 °C.

Last 25 years

Temperatures in the lower troposphere have increased at somewhere between 0.08 and 0.22 °/decade since 1979. Just like the surface record, the average temperature rise is not linear, but has superimposed on it rises and falls due to natural variability, most notably El nino's. Over the same period the surface record shows a warming of approximately 0.15 °C/ decade.

Theories to explain temperature change

The climate system varies both through natural, "internal" processes as well as in response to variations in "external forcing" from both human and non-human causes, including changes in the Earth's orbit around the Sun (Milankovitch cycles), solar activity , and volcanic emissions as well as greenhouse gases.

Climatologists accept that the earth has warmed recently. Somewhat more controversial is what may have caused this change.

Greenhouse gas theory

The hypothesis that increases or decreases in greenhouse gas concentration would lead to higher or lower global mean temperature was first postulated in the late 19th century by Swedish chemist and 1903 Nobel Laureate Svante Arrhenius, largely as an attempt to explain ice ages. At the time his peers largely rejected his theory.

The theory that human greenhouse gas emissions are contributing to the warming of the Earth's atmosphere has gained many adherents and some opponents in the scientific community within the past 25 years. The IPCC, which was established to assess the risk of human-induced climate change, attributes most of the recent warming to human activities. The United States National Academy of Sciences also endorsed the theory. Atmospheric physicist Richard Lindzen and other skeptics oppose aspects of the theory.

There are many subtle aspects to the question. Atmospheric scientists know that adding carbon dioxide (CO_2) to an atmosphere, with no other changes, will tend to make a planet's surface warmer. But there is an important amount of water vapor (humidity, clouds) in the Earth's atmosphere, and water vapor is a strong greenhouse gas. If adding CO_2 to the atmosphere changes processes that regulate the amount of water vapor in the Earth's atmosphere, that could have a profound effect on the climate: more water vapor means more warmth.

The effect of clouds is also critical. Clouds have competing effects on the climate; everyone has noticed that surface temperature drops when a cloud passes overhead on an otherwise hot, sunny summer day. So clouds cool the surface by reflecting sunlight back into space. But many people have also noticed that clear winter nights tend to be colder than cloudy winter nights. That is because clouds also radiate heat back to the surface of the Earth. If CO_2 changes the amount of distribution of clouds, it could have various complex effects on the climate.

Given this, it is not correct to imagine that there is a debate is between those who "believe in" and "oppose" the theory that adding CO_2 to the Earth's atmosphere will result in warmer surface temperatures on Earth, on average. Rather, the debate is about what the *net* effect of the addition of CO_2 will be, and whether changes in water vapor, clouds, and so on will *cancel out* its warming effect. The observed warming of the Earth over the past 50 years appears to be at odds with the skeptics' theory that climate feedbacks will cancel out the CO_2 warming.

Scientists have also studied this issue with computer models of the climate. These models are accepted by the scientific community as being valid only after it has been shown that they do a good job of simulating known climate variations, such as the difference between summer and winter, the North Atlantic Oscillation, or El Nino. It is universally found that those climate models that pass these tests also always predict that the net effect of adding CO_2 will be a warmer climate in the future, when all the water vapor and cloud changes are taken into account. The amount of predicted warming varies by model, however, which probably reflects the way different models depict clouds differently. Skeptics of "global warming" say that the models are inaccurate, but have been unable to produce a model of the climate that does not predict that temperatures will increase in the future. Thus, the skeptics' theory that climate feedbacks will eliminate any CO_2 warming effect is not supported by either the observations or any credible model.

CO_2 at Mauna Loa since 1958

Coal-burning power plants, automobile exhausts, factory smokestacks, and other waste vents of the human environment contribute about 22 billion tons of carbon dioxide (corresponding to 6 billion tons of pure carbon) and other greenhouse gases into the earth's atmosphere each year. The atmospheric concentration of CO_2 has increased by 31% above pre-industrial levels since 1750. This is considerably higher than at any time during the last 420,000 years, the period for which reliable data has been extracted from ice cores. From less direct geological evidence it is believed that CO_2 values this high were last attained 40 million years ago. About three-quarters of the anthropogenic emissions of CO_2 to the atmosphere during the past 20 years is due to fossil fuel burning. The rest is predominantly due to land-use change, especially deforestation.

"Greenhouse gases" get their name because they trap radiant energy from the sun that would otherwise be re-radiated back into space, by analogy with the glass panes in a greenhouse. The analogy, however, is a false one: the effects are different. The natural greenhouse effect that tempers the earth's climate is not at issue in the debate over global warming. Without it, temperatures would drop by approximately 30°C, the oceans would freeze and life as we know it would be impossible. What climatologists are concerned about, rather, is that increased levels of greenhouse gases in the atmosphere might cause more heat to be trapped.

Increases in CO_2 measured since 1958 at Mauna Loa show a monotonically increasing atmospheric concentration of CO_2. In fact, it is clear that the increase is faster than linear. On March 21, 2004, it was reported that the concentration in ppm reached 376ppm in 2003. South Pole records show similar growth.

Solar variation theory

Various hypotheses have been proposed to link terrestrial temperature variations to solar variations. The meteorological community has responded with skepticism, in part because theories of this nature have come and gone over the course of the 20th century.

Sami Solanki, the director of the Max Planck Institute for Solar System Research in Göttingen, Germany said:

> The sun has been at its strongest over the past 60 years and may now be affecting global temperatures.... He continued: the brighter sun and higher levels of so-called "greenhouse gases" both contributed to the change in the Earth's temperature, but it was impossible to say which had the greater impact.

Willie Soon and Sallie Baliunas of the Harvard Observatory correlated historical sunspot counts with temperature proxies. They report that when there are fewer sunspots, the earth cooled — and that when there are more sunspots the earth warmed.

The theories have usually represented one of three types:

— Solar irradiance changes directly affecting the climate. This is generally considered unlikely, as the variations seem to be small

— Variations in the ultraviolet component having an effect. The UV component varies by more than the total.

— Effects mediated by changes in cosmic rays (which are affected by the solar wind, which is affected by the solar output) such as changes in cloud cover.

Although correlations often can be found, the mechanism behind these correlations is a matter of speculation. Many of these speculative accounts have fared badly over time, and in a paper "Solar activity and terrestrial climate: an analysis of some purported correlations". Peter Laut demonstrates problems with some of the most popular, notably those by Svensmark and by Lassen.

In 1991, Knud Lassen of the Danish Meteorological Institute in Copenhagen and his colleague Eigil Friis-Christensen found a strong correlation between the length of the solar cycle and temperature changes throughout the northern hemisphere. Initially, they used sunspot and temperature measurements from 1861 to 1989, but later found that climate records dating back four centuries supported their findings. This relationship appeared to account for nearly 80 per cent of the measured temperature changes over this period. Sallie Baliunas, an astronomer at the Harvard-Smithsonian Center for Astrophysics, has been among the supporters of the theory that changes in the sun "can account for major climate changes on Earth for the past 300 years, including part of the recent surge of global warming."

On May 6, 2000, however, *New Scientist* magazine reported that Lassen and astrophysicist Peter Thejll had updated Lassen's 1991 research and found that while the solar cycle still accounts for about half the temperature rise since 1900, it fails to explain a rise of 0.4 °C since 1980. "The curves diverge after 1980," Thejll said, "and it's a startlingly large deviation. Something else is acting on the climate. ... It has the fingerprints of the greenhouse effect."

Later that same year, Peter Stott and other researchers at the Hadley Centre in the United Kingdom published a paper in which they reported on the most comprehensive model simulations to date of the climate of the 20th century. Their study looked at both *natural forcing agents* (solar variations and volcanic emissions) as well as *anthropogenic forcing* (greenhouse gases and sulphate aerosols). Like Lassen and Thejll, they found that the *natural* factors accounted for gradual warming to about 1960 followed by a return to late 19th-century temperatures, consistent with the gradual change in solar forcing throughout the 20th century and volcanic activity during the past few decades. These factors alone, however, could not account for the warming in recent decades.

Similarly, anthropogenic forcing alone was insufficient to explain the 1910–1945 warming, but was necessary to simulate the warming since 1976. Stott's team found that combining all of these factors enabled them to closely simulate global temperature changes throughout the 20th century. They predicted that continued greenhouse gas emissions would cause additional future temperature increases "at a rate similar to that observed in recent decades."

A graphical representation of the relationship between natural and anthropogenic factors contributing to climate change appears in "Climate Change 2001: The Scientific Basis," a report by the Intergovernmental Panel on Climate Change (IPCC).

Others

Various other hypotheses have been proposed, including but not limited to:

- The current increase in temperature is predicted by the Milankovitch cycles theory, in which gradual changes in the Earth's orbit around the Sun and changes in the Earth's axial tilt affect the amount of solar energy reaching the Earth.
- The warming is within the range of natural variation and needs no particular explanation

— The warming is a consequence of coming out of a prior cool period — the Little ice age — and needs no other explanation.

Some skeptics would claim that the warming trend itself is not valid, and therefore does not need any explanation.

Jurassic global warming

It is thought by geologists that the Earth experienced global warming in the early Jurassic period, with average temperatures rising by 5° Celsius (9° Fahrenheit). Research by the Open University published in *Geology* indicates that this caused the weathering of rocks to be speeded up by 400%, a process that took around 150,000 years to return carbon dioxide levels to normal.

Climate models

The most recent climate models produce a good simulation of the global temperature change over the last century. Climate simulations do not unambiguously attribute the warming that occurred from approximately 1910 to 1945 to either natural variation or to anthropogenic forcing. All models show that the warming occurring from approximately 1975 to 2000 is largely anthropogenic. These conclusions depend on the accuracy of the models used and on the correct estimation of the external factors.

The majority of scientists agree that important climate processes are incorrectly accounted for by the climate models but don't think that better models would change the conclusion.

Critics point out that there are unspecified flaws in the models and unspecified external factors not taken into consideration that could change the conclusion above. Some unidentified critics say that the climate simulations are unable to fit the water vapor feedback, and handle clouds. Some indirect solar effects may be very important and are not accounted for by the models. Or then again, they might not be important at all.

Potential effects

Many public policy organizations, governments, and individuals are concerned that global warming could potentially harm the environment and global agriculture. This is a matter of considerable controversy, with environmentalist groups typically emphasizing the possible dangers and groups close to industry questioning the climate models and consequences of global warming — and funding scientists to do so.

Due to potential effects on human health and economy due to the impact on the environment, global warming is a cause of great concern. Some important environmental changes have been observed and linked to global warming.

Examples of secondary evidence of global warming—lessened snow cover, rising sea levels, weather changes— are examples of consequences of global warming that may influence not only human activities but also the ecosystems. Increasing global temperature means that ecosystems may change; some species may be forced out of their habitats (possibly to extinction) because of changing conditions, while others may spread. Few of the terrestrial ecoregions on Earth could expect to be unaffected.

Another cause of great concern to some is sea level rise. Sea levels are rising 1 to 2 centimetres (around half an inch) per decade, and some Pacific Ocean island nations, such as Tuvalu are working out the details of their expected eventual evacuation.

Global warming causes the sea level to rise because sea water expands as it warms and through thinning of the polar ice caps and sea ice and reduction of glaciers. The IPCC TAR says: "Global mean sea level is projected to rise by 0.09 to 0.88 metres between 1990 and 2100, for the full range of SRES scenarios. This is due primarily to thermal expansion and loss of mass from glaciers and ice caps".

As the climate gets hotter, evaporation will increase. This will cause heavier rainfall and more erosion. Many people think that it could result in more extreme weather as global warming progresses. The IPCC TAR says: "...global average water vapour concentration and precipitation are projected to increase during the 21st century. By the second half of the 21st century, it is likely that precipitation will have increased over northern mid- to high latitudes and Antarctica in winter. At low latitudes there are both regional increases and decreases over land areas. Larger year to year variations in precipitation are very likely over most areas where an increase in mean precipitation is projected".

Global warming can also have other, less obvious effects. The North Atlantic drift, for instance, is driven by temperature changes. It seems that it is diminishing as the climate grows warmer, and this means that areas like Scandinavia and Britain that are warmed by the drift might face a colder climate in spite of the general global warming. It is now feared that global warming may be able to trigger the type of abrupt massive temperature shifts which bracketed the Younger Dryas period.

Global warming will probably extend the favourable zones for vectors conveying infectious disease, such as Malaria, Dengue fever, or Yellow fever.

However, global warming may also have positive effects, since higher temperatures and higher CO_2 concentrations may improve the ecosystems' productivity. Satellite data shows that the productivity of the Northern Hemisphere has increased since 1982. On the other hand, an increase in the total amount of biomass produced is not necessarily all good, since biodiversity can still decrease even though a smaller number of species are flourishing. Similarly, from the human economic viewpoint, an increase in total biomass but a decrease in crop harvests would be a net disadvantage. In addition, IPCC models predict that higher CO_2 concentrations would only spur growth of flora up to a point, because in many regions the limiting factors are water or nutrients, not temperature or CO_2; after that, though greenhouse effects and warming would continue there would be no compensatory increase in growth.

Relation between global warming and ozone depletion

Although they are often interlinked in the popular press, the connection between global warming and ozone depletion is not strong. There are three areas of linkage:

— Global warming from CO_2 radiative forcing is expected (perhaps somewhat surprisingly) to *cool* the stratosphere. This, in turn, would lead to a relative *increase* in ozone depletion and the frequency of ozone holes.

— Conversely, ozone depletion represents a radiative forcing of the climate system. There are two opposed effects: reduced ozone allows more solar radiation to penetrate, thus warming the troposphere. But a colder stratosphere emits less long-wave radiation, tending to cool the troposphere. Overall, the cooling dominates: the IPCC concludes that observed stratospheric O_3 losses over the past two decades have caused a negative forcing of the surface-troposphere system.

— One of the strongest predictions of the GW theory is that the stratosphere should cool. However, although this is observed, it is difficult to use it for attribution (for example, warming induced by increased solar radiation would not have this upper cooling effect) because similar cooling is caused by ozone depletion.

GLOBAL WARMING CONTROVERSY

The global warming controversy is a long-running dispute about human effects - past, present and future - on climate. The starting point is whether there has been significant global warming caused by industrial emissions of carbon dioxide. But this alone would be a scientific argument confined to the scientific press. The point that leads to major controversy - because it could have significant economic impacts - is whether action (usually, restrictions on the use of fossil fuels to reduce CO2 emmissions) should be taken now or in the near future.

"Proponents"' position

Supporters of the global warming theory assert that:

— the IPCC reports correctly summarise the state of climate science

— the historical temperature record shows a rise of 0.4-0.8 oC over the last 100 years

— this rise is unprecedented in the temperature record of the past 1000 years

— climate models can reproduce this trend, but only when using greenhouse gas forcing

— attribution of recent climate change shows that the rise can be attributed to human emissions of greenhouse gases

— climate models predict more warming, and other climate effects (sea level rise, etc) in the future

— there is a scientific consensus behind all of the above

— humankind is performing a great geophysical experiment and if it turns out badly - however that is defined - we cannot undo it.

"Proponents" of global warming tend to support the IPCC position and thus represent a broadly unified viewpoint, though with considerable differences over what action should be taken. Optionally, supporters may go on to point out that there is a good chance that the future changes may be undesirable, and that planning to avoid or mitigate them would be a good idea.

Participation in the IPCC process does not imply endorsement of it. However, only 2 of the 120 contributing authors to the IPCC TAR are known to have voiced any complaint.

Opponents' position

There are many reasons for opposition to the global warming beliefs, and these major positions are independent of each other. Some items in this list may contradict others.

— IPCC reports do not reflect the science or reality.

— Using "consensus" as evidence is an appeal to the majority argument rather than scientific discussion.

— Earth's climate has been both colder and warmer than today, and these changes are adequately explained by mechanisms that do not involve human greenhouse gas emissions.

— There is no significant global warming relative to the expected natural trends.

— A small amount of global warming would be benign or even beneficial.

— Climate science can not make definitive predictions yet, since the computer models used to make these predictions are still evolving and do not yet take into account recently discovered feedback mechanisms.

— Global warming studies have errors or have not been reproduced.

Members of this faction give more weight to data such as paleoclimatic studies, temperature measurements made from weather balloons, and satellites which they claim show less warming than surface land and sea records.

"Opponents" tend to define themselves in terms of opposition to the IPCC position and do not have a unified viewpoint for anything.

Scope of the controversy

The controversy occurs almost entirely within the press and political arenas. In the scientific press and amongst climate researchers, there is little "controversy" about global warming, only a desire to investigate a scientific problem and determine its consequences. As Kevin E. Trenberth writes:

> In 1995 the IPCC assessment concluded that "the balance of evidence suggests that there is a discernible human influence on global climate". Since then the evidence has become much stronger ... Thus the headline in IPCC (2001) is "There is new and stronger evidence that most of the warming observed over the last 50 years is attributable to human activities"... While some changes arising from global warming are benign or even beneficial, the economic effects of the weather extremes are substantial and clearly warrant attention in policy debates... Consequently, there is a strong case for slowing down the projected rates of climate change from human influences.

Trenberth also provides evidence for the controversy that occurs when science meets the political arene:

> The SPM was approved line by line by governments... The argument here is that the scientists determine what can said, but the governments determine how it can best be said. Negotiations occur over wording to ensure accuracy, balance, clarity of message, and relevance to understanding and policy. The IPCC process is dependent on the good will of the participants in producing a balanced assessment. However, in Shanghai, it appeared that there were attempts to blunt, and perhaps obfuscate, the messages in the report, most notably by Saudi Arabia. This led to very protracted debates over wording on even bland and what should be uncontroversial text... The most contentious paragraph in the IPCC (2001) SPM was the concluding one on attribution. After much debate the following was carefully crafted: "In the light of new evidence, and taking into account the remaining uncertainties, most of the observed warming over the last 50 years is likely to have been due to the increase in greenhouse gas concentrations."

Counting experts

The proportion of scientists who support or oppose any of the global warming theories is a matter of controversy in its own right. Environmentalists and their allies claim virtually unanimous support for the global warming theory from the scientific community. Opponents maintain that it is the other way around, claiming that the overwhelming majority of scientists either dismiss global warming altogether or merely consider it "unproven".

Arguments around the world

The arguments over global warming are viewed differently in different parts of the world. In Europe for example the environmentalist argument over Global warming has gained wider acceptance than in other parts of the world, most notably North America.

Beneficial or detrimental

There is also disagreement on whether the effects of global warming will be beneficial or detrimental. Many researchers predict disastrous consequences for a warming of 1.5 to 7 degrees Celsius. The UN's Intergovernmental Panel on Climate Change (IPCC) predicts such a warming is likely within the 21st century, unless severe measures are taken. Other researchers feel that up to 1.5 degrees Celsius of warming would increase crop yields and stabilize weather. Many of these doubt a larger warming is likely. In response, some advocates of strong early measures (well beyond Kyoto) note that the belief in beneficial effects and the doubt that a large warming is possible should be independent if these conclusions were in fact neutrally derived from scientific research.

Wait and see

Others suggest that a "wait and see" strategy disadvantages 3.5 billion people in favor of narrow advantage for a few growing regions and developed nations. However, those others have not provided details for their claims nor the advantages given to the other 3 billion people.

An unstable world

New findings have suggested that the earth's climate system is inherently unstable, and that global warming could thus precipitate non-linear sudden climate shifts, as have been discovered to have occurred within the earth's past. Ocean circulation, believed to be the key to such climate shifts, has been observed to be slowing, causing alarm among oceanographers. As briefly mentioned before some scientists fear that the Gulf Stream which conveys warm water from the Caribbean Sea across the Atlantic Ocean and is partly responsible for the relative mildness of northern Europe's climate. There is a fear that it could be reduced or stopped altogether by the decreased salt content in the sea water, which would result from global warming. Which could cause temperatures in northern europe to drop.

The US National Academy of Sciences issued a report on this phenomenon in 2002, titled *Abrupt Climate Change - Inevitable Surprises.* "It is important not to be fatalistic about the threats posed by abrupt climate change," it stated. "Societies have faced both gradual and abrupt climate changes for millennia and have learned to adapt through various mechanisms, such as moving indoors, developing irrigation for crops, and migrating away from inhospitable regions. Nevertheless, because climate change will likely continue in the coming decades, denying the likelihood or downplaying the relevance of past abrupt events could be costly."

Recent reports

However, the US National Academy of Sciences, both in its 2002 report to President George W. Bush, and in its latest publications, has strongly endorsed evidence of an average global temperature increase in the 20th century and stated that human activity is heavily implicated in causing this increase. The American Meteorological Society (AMS statement, the American Geophysical Union (AGU statement, and other scientific societies have issued similar declarations. John Christy, who is usually placed in the skeptics camp, has signed the AGU statement on climate change.

Advocates of the global warming hypothesis who predict adverse consequences from as little as 1.5 degrees Celsius of warming nearly all support the Kyoto Protocol as a countermeasure.

KYOTO PROTOCOL

The Kyoto Protocol is a proposed amendment to an international treaty on global warming — the United Nations Framework Convention on Climate Change (UNFCCC). Countries which ratify this protocol will commit to reduce their emissions of carbon dioxide and other greenhouse gases, which are linked to global warming. It also reaffirms sections of the UNFCCC.

The formal name of the proposed agreement is the Kyoto Protocol to the United Nations Framework Convention on Climate Change.

It was negotiated in Kyoto, Japan in December 1997, opened for signature on March 16, 1998, and closed on March 15, 1999.

Details of the agreement

According to a press release from the United Nations Environment Programme:

> "The Kyoto Protocol is a legally binding agreement under which industrialized countries will reduce their collective emissions of greenhouse gases by 5.2% compared to the

> year 1990 (but note that, compared to the emissions levels that would be expected by 2010 without the Protocol, this target represents a 29% cut). The goal is to lower overall emissions from six greenhouse gases - carbon dioxide, methane, nitrous oxide, sulphur hexafluoride, HFCs, and PFCs - calculated as an average over the five-year period of 2008-12. National targets range from 8% reductions for the European Union and some others to 7% for the US, 6% for Japan, 0% for Russia, and permitted increases of 8% for Australia and 10% for Iceland."

It is a protocol to the United Nations Framework Convention on Climate Change (UNFCCC), which was adopted in Rio de Janeiro in 1992. All parties to the UNFCCC can sign or ratify the Kyoto Protocol, while non-parties to the UNFCCC cannot. The Kyoto Protocol was adopted at the third session of the Conference of Parties (COP) to the UNFCCC in 1997 in Kyoto, Japan.

Most provisions of the Kyoto Protocol apply to developed countries, listed in Annex I to the UNFCCC.

Financial commitments

The Protocol also reaffirms the principle that developed countries have to pay, and supply technology to, other countries for climate-related studies and projects. This was originally agreed in the UNFCCC.

Emissions trading

General article: emissions trading

Each Annex I country has agreed to limit emissions to the levels described in the protocol, but many countries have limits that are set above their current production. These "extra amounts" can be purchased by other countries on the open market. So, for instance, Russia currently easily meets its targets, and can sell off its *credits* for millions of dollars to countries that don't yet meet their targets, Canada for instance. This rewards countries that meet their targets, and provides financial incentives to others to do so as soon as possible. Countries also receive credits through various shared "clean energy" programs and "carbon sinks" in the form of forests and other systems that remove carbon from the atmosphere.

Washington D.C.-based NGO, in their report "Getting It Right: Emerging Markets for Storing Carbon in Forests", assumes values of $30-40/ton in the US and $70-80/ton in Europe. On April 18, 2001, The Netherlands purchased credits for 4 megatons of carbon dioxide emissions from Poland, Romania, and the Czech Republic; this was part of the ERUPT procurement procedure. These purchase agreements however contained conditions precedent, e.g. referring to the financing of the underlying projects. Since several of these conditions have not been met, the amount of purchased credits has since then decreased.

Status of the agreement

As of February 2002, the agreement had been ratified by 104 countries, representing 43.9% of emissions. Countries do not need to sign the protocol in order to ratify it—signing is a symbolic act only. A total of 19 countries had signed the agreement but not ratified it. The remaining 58 parties to the UNFCCC had neither signed nor ratified the protocol. According to the terms of the protocol, it enters into force "on the ninetieth day after the date on which not less than 55 Parties to the Convention, incorporating Parties included in Annex I which accounted in total for at least 55 per cent of the total carbon dioxide emissions for 1990 of the Parties included in Annex I, have deposited their instruments of ratification, acceptance, approval or accession."

Revisions

The protocol left several issues open, to be decided later by the COP. COP6 attempted to resolve these issues at its meeting in the Hague in late 2000, but was unable to reach an agreement due to disputes between the European Union on the one hand (which favoured a tougher agreement) and the United States, Canada, Japan and Australia on the other (which wanted the agreement to be less demanding and more flexible).

In 2001, a continuation of the previous meeting (COP6bis) was held in Bonn where the required decisions were adopted. After some concessions, the supporters of the protocol (led by the European Union) managed to get Japan and Russia in as well by allowing more use of carbon dioxide sinks.

Current positions of governments

As of 2002, 104 countries have ratified the protocol, including Canada, People's Republic of China, India, Japan, New Zealand, and the twenty-five countries of the European Union, as well as Romania and Bulgaria.

As of 2004, Russia is in the process of ratifying the protocol, after the Russian government recommended that Parliament ratify the protocol on September 30, 2004.

18 other countries have signed the protocol but not ratified it. Of those seven are Annex I countries:

— Australia (not intending to ratify)

— Croatia

— Liechtenstein

— Monaco

— Switzerland — Switzerland passed the CO2 law on — October 8, 1999 which should allow it to achieve its target of 8% below 1990 levels by 2010. The Kyoto Protocol has been ratified by the Senate but not yet by the House of Representatives.

— Ukraine — Ukraine is expected to ratify the protocol.

— United States — The US, the largest emitter of greenhouse gases, does not intend to ratify the protocol.

Some countries that have signed but not yet ratified are: Egypt, Indonesia, Israel, Kazakhstan, Marshall Islands, Niger, Philippines, Saint Lucia, Saint Vincent and the Grenadines, and the Solomon Islands.

Position of the former Soviet bloc

On 22 October 2004 the Kyoto treaty was ratified by Russia's lower house of parliament, the Duma. It is anticipated that ratification by the upper house of parliament, and its signing into law by President Putin should not encounter any obstacles. President Putin had earlier decided in favour of the protocol in September 2004, along with the Russian cabinet It had been sent to the Duma for ratification. Mosnews had reported that Putin "unambiguously backed" the protocol. This was consistent with the results of the World Climate Change Conference held in Moscow in late 2003.

Mosnews had also pointed out that "Russian scientists, asked for their expert opinion directly by President Putin, also called the Kyoto Protocol a scientifically unfounded nonsense." ITAR-TASS reported "Earlier, Russia's influential Academy of Sciences (RAN) said the government's decision to approve the Kyoto Protocol was "purely political," and that it had no scientific justification." It is not clear quite where these russian experts get their scientific opinions - at the wccc2003 A.N. Illarionov asked 10 fairly naive questions on climate change which were immeadiately answered. Nonetheless, months later A.N. Illarionov was still claiming not to have been answered.

The Kyoto Protocol limits emissions to a percentage increase or decrease from their 1990 levels. Since 1990 the economies of most countries in the former Soviet Union have collapsed, as have their greenhouse gas emissions. Because of this, Russia should have no problem meeting its commitments under Kyoto, as its current emission levels are substantially below its targets. Indeed, it may be able to benefit from selling emissions credits to other countries in the Kyoto Protocol, which are currently using more than their target levels of emissions. For these reasons, Russia had been expected to ratify the agreement, which would have been sufficient to bring the accord into force.

UN and European backers of the Kyoto Protocol who had hoped Russia would commit to ratification were previously disappointed in September 2003 when at a Moscow conference Putin indicated his reluctance to sign. Among the reasons for this were the outspoken criticism of Russian scientists for the fundamental scientific foundation of Kyoto - the hypothesis that CO_2 is a major driver of world climate change. Finally, on September 30, 2004, the Russian Cabinet sent the protocol for ratification to the Parliament.

The issue of Russian ratification continues to be particularly closely watched in the international community, as Russia's ratification should bring the accord into force. Conversely, should any difficulty arise with Russia's ratification, combined with the United States' decision not to ratify, it would likely preclude the agreement entering into force at all.

The Ukrainian economy, like the Russian economy, is such that meeting Kyoto commitments should initially be easy, and Ukraine is expected to ratify the protocol.

Position of the European Union

On May 31, 2002, all fifteen then-members of the European Union deposited the relevant ratification paperwork at the UN. The EU produces around 21% of global greenhouse gas emissions, and has agreed to a cut, on average, by 8% from 1990 emission levels. The EU has consistently been one of the major supporters of the Kyoto Protocol, negotiating hard to get wavering countries on board.

In December, 2002, the EU created a system of emissions trading in an effort to meet these tough targets. Quotas were introduced in six key industries: energy, steel, cement, glass, brick making, and paper/cardboard. There are also fines for member nations that fail to meet their obligations, starting at €40/ton of carbon dioxide in 2005, and rising to €100/ton in 2008. Current EU projections suggest that by 2008 the EU will be at 4.7% below 1990 levels.

Position of the United States

The United States, although a signatory to the protocol, has neither ratified nor withdrawn from the protocol. The protocol is non-binding over the United States unless ratified. On June 25, 1997, before the Kyoto Protocol was to be negotiated, the U.S. Senate passed by a 95-0 vote the Byrd-Hagel Resolution, which stated the sense of the Senate was that the United States should not be a signatory to any protocol that that did not include binding targets and timetables for developing as well as industrialized nations or "would result in serious harm to the economy of the United States". Disregarding the Senate Resolution, on November 12, 1998, Vice President Al Gore symbolically signed the protocol. Aware of the Senate's view of the protocol, the Clinton Administration never submitted the protocol for ratification.

The current President, George W. Bush, has indicated that he does not intend to submit the treaty for ratification, not because he doesn't support the general idea, but because he is not happy with the details of the treaty. For example, he does not support the split between Annex I countries and others. Bush said of the treaty:

> "The world's second-largest emitter of greenhouse gases is China. Yet, China was entirely exempted from the requirements of the Kyoto Protocol. This is a challenge that requires a 100 percent effort; ours, and the rest of the world's. America's unwillingness to embrace a flawed treaty should not be read by our friends and allies as any

> abdication of responsibility. To the contrary, my administration is committed to a leadership role on the issue of climate change. Our approach must be consistent with the long-term goal of stabilizing greenhouse gas concentrations in the atmosphere."

China emits 2,893 million metric tons of CO_2 per year (2.3 tons per capita). This compares to 5,410 million from the USA (20.1 tons per capita), and 3,171 million from the EU (8.5 tons per capita). China has since ratified the Kyoto Protocol, and is expected to become an Annex I country within the next decade. The US Natural Resources Defense Council, stated in June 2001 that: "By switching from coal to cleaner energy sources, initiating energy efficiency programs, and restructuring its economy, China has reduced its carbon dioxide emissions 17 percent since 1997". In June 2002, the American Environmental Protection Agency (EPA) released the "Climate Action Report 2002". Some observers have interpreted this report as being supportive of the protocol, although the report itself does not explicitly endorse the protocol.

The prospect of the US staying outside the agreement influenced a number of other countries including Australia, Japan, and Canada to discuss whether they should ratify the agreement, putting themselves at a competitive disadvantage with the USA. While Japan and Canada ultimately decided to ratify the protocol, Australia's current government has said it will not ratify. Although the major opposition parties have committed to ratification if in a position to do so, the Government retained power in the 2004 election so it seems unlikely that Australia will support the treaty in the near future.

Position of Canada

On December 17, 2002, Canada ratified the treaty. This was however opposed by groups of businesses, non-governmental climate scientists and energy concerns, using arguments similar to those being used in the US. However an additional twist is involved. The US is Canada's major trading partner (and vice versa), so with Canadian companies having to pay for emissions, and US companies not, the fear is that Canadian companies will not be able to compete on a fair trading ground. In one example a company can sell natural gas to the US to be burned in an electrical plant to produce electricity. That gas, burned in the US, is not subject to "Kyoto tax". However if that same plant were operated in Canada, the gas would be taxed as it was burned. That would result in the same electricity costing more if produced locally.

The result is an ongoing "war of words", primarily between the government of Alberta (a major oil and gas producer) and the federal government, although non-governmental climate scientists are becoming increasingly vocal in the press in their opposition to the treaty. This is largely due to the fact that these scientists were shut out of the consultation process while environmental pressure groups were allowed to take part broadly. It also appears that the federal government will ask for additional credits for "clean" fuels sold to the United States, most notably natural gas.

A September 2004 showed that support in Canada for the Kyoto protocol is around 70% and now includes a majority of Albertans as well, a province that was initially a hub for anti-Kyoto politics. In fact, it is now British Columbia where the support for the Kyoto protocol is the least in Canada but even there the majority is in favour.

Support for Kyoto

Advocates of the Kyoto Protocol claim that reducing these emissions is crucially important; carbon dioxide, they believe, is causing the earth's atmosphere to heat up. This is supported by attribution analysis. Most prominent among advocates of Kyoto have been the European Union and many environmentalist organizations. The United Nations and some individual nations' scientific advisory bodies have also issued reports favoring the Kyoto Protocol.

Opposition to Kyoto

Some critics say there are problems with the underlying science. The 1997 Leipzig Declaration called the Kyoto Protocol "dangerously simplistic, quite ineffective, and economically destructive to jobs and standards-of-living". Most of the signers of the Leipzig Declaration are non-scientists or lack credentials in the specific field of climate research.

In June of 2003, an open letter was written to Canada's then-future prime minister, Paul Martin, signed by 46 climate experts from six countries - Martin has yet to respond. A previous open letter was signed by 27 climate experts and sent to then-current Prime Minister, Jean Chrétien.

Some opponents argue that the protocol does not go far *enough* to curb greenhouse emissions, and the standards it sets would be totally ineffective at curbing or even slowing climate change. In addition, there have been recent scientific challenges to the idea of carbon credits, planting "Kyoto forests" or tree farms to reduce total carbon dioxide output. Recent evidence shows that this may in fact increase carbon dioxide emissions for the first 10 years, due to the growth pattern of young forests and the effect it has on soil-trapped carbon dioxide. Several industrial countries have made carbon credits an important part of their strategies for reducing their net greenhouse gas outputs, further calling into question the effectiveness of the protocols.

To evaluate the effectiveness of the Kyoto protocol, it is necessary to compare global warming with and without the agreement. Several independent authors agree that the impact of the Kyoto protocol on global warming is very small (a reduction of 0.15 Celsius degrees by 2100, out of a projected total change of 1.4 to 5.8 Celsius degrees). Even some defenders of the Kyoto Protocol agree that the impact of it is small, but they view it as a first step, with more political than practical importance, for future reductions, perhaps of up to 70%.

The Kyoto Protocol can also be evaluated by comparing costs and gains. Several economic analyses were made that show that the Kyoto Protocol is more expensive than the global warming that it avoids. Defenders of the Kyoto Protocol argue however that while the initial greenhouse gas cuts may have little effect, they set the political precedent for bigger (and more effective) cuts in the future. Also, they demonstrate commitment to the precautionary principle.

Some theorists predict that even if the world's leading industrial nations agree to reduce their "greenhouse" emissions as mandated by the Kyoto Protocol, it is likely that there would be no net change in emissions worldwide. As the industrialized countries cut their demand for fossil fuels, the law of supply and demand will tend to cause the world prices of coal, oil and gas go down, making fuel use more affordable for poorer nations. These theorists predict increased fuel use (primarily coal) in the "non-Annex I" countries, tending to offset the reductions of the "Annex I" countries.

INTERNATIONAL ENVIRONMENTAL LAW

International environmental law is the body of international law that concerns the protection of the global environment. There have been many legally-binding international agreements concerning the protection of the environment, but in this area of international law soft law is more common than normal. Some basic principles of international environmental law are:

- the precautionary principle
- the polluter pays principle
- the principle of sustaintable development

Important cases have included the various nuclear test cases (New Zealand vs. France) before the International Court of Justice.

5

OZONE LAYER DEPLETION

OZONE

Ozone (O_3) is a molecule consisting of three oxygen atoms. At standard temperature and pressure Ozone is a blue gas. Ozone forms a dark blue liquid, below -112 °C, and a dark blue solid, below -193 °C. Ozone is a powerful oxidizing agent, and is unstable, decaying to ordinary oxygen through the reaction:

$$2O_3 \rightarrow 3O_2$$

Ozone is highly corrosive and is a poisonous substance and a common pollutant. It has a sharp, pungent odor. It is present in low concentrations throughout the Earth's atmosphere. It is also formed from O_2 by electrical discharges, e.g., lightning, and by action of high energy electromagnetic radiation. Some electrical equipment generates levels of ozone that a human can easily smell; this is especially true if there is a spark gap or a very high voltage.

The highest levels of ozone in the atmosphere are in the stratosphere, in a region also known as the ozone layer. Here it filters out much ultraviolet light from the Sun that would be harmful to most forms of life. The standard way to express ozone amounts in the atmosphere is by using Dobson units. Ozone used in industry is measured in ppm (OSHA exposure limits for example), and percent weight. Ozone was discovered by Christian Friedrich Schonbein in 1840.

Stratospheric ozone

Ozone is notable for its ability to absorb UV-B radiation. Ozone is created naturally within the ozone layer. Ozone depletion and ozone holes occur because of chlorofluorocarbons and other upper atmospheric contaminants.

Ozone in the earth's atmosphere is generally created by ultraviolet light which breaks apart O_2 molecules, creating atomic oxygen. The atomic oxygen then combines with an unbroken molecule, to create O_3. Sometimes the individual oxygen atoms will combine with N_2 to create a nitrogen oxide; which, when affected by visible light, may create ozone.

When ultraviolet light hits ozone it splits into a molecule of O_2 and an atom of atomic oxygen, a continuing process called the ozone-oxygen cycle. This cycle can be disrupted by the presence of atomic chlorine, fluorine or bromine in the atmosphere; these elements are found in certain stable compounds, especially chlorofluorocarbons (CFCs) which may find their way to the stratosphere and there be liberated by the action of ultraviolet light on them. The NO_x cycle for the formation of Ozone can also be broken by the presence of atmospheric water, reducing NO_x to a more stable form.

Ozone as a pollutant Use in industry

Ozone can be used for bleaching substances and for killing bacteria. Many municipal drinking water systems kill bacteria with ozone instead of the more common chlorine. Ozone does not form organochlorine compounds, but it also does not remain in the water after treatment, so some systems introduce a small amount of chlorine to prevent bacterial growth in the pipes.

Industrially, Ozone is used to:

- disinfect water before it is bottled,
- chemically attack contaminants in water (iron, arsenic, hydrogen sulfide, nitrites, and complex organics lumped together as "color"),

— provide an aid to flocculation (a process of agglomeration of molecules, which aids in filtration... this is where the iron and arsenic get removed),

— clean and bleach fabrics (the latter use is patented),

— assist in processing plastics to allow adhesion of inks,

— age rubber samples to determine the useful life of a batch of rubber.

Use in medicine

Ozone, along with hypochlorite ions, is naturally produced by white blood cells and the roots of marigolds as a means of destroying foreign bodies. When ozone breaks down it gives rise to oxygen free radicals, which are highly reactive and damage or destroy most organic molecules.

Ozone has a number of medical uses. It can be used to affect the body's antioxidant-prooxidant balance, since the body usually reacts to its presence by producing antioxidant enzymes.

Ozone therapy has blossomed into a thriving field of alternative medicine, and there are a host of claimed applications above and beyond what has actually been verified by studies. Ozone treatments are dangerous, however, since ozone is highly corrosive. In the USA ozone therapy is illegal, as the FDA has not approved its use on humans. At least one death has been attributed to application of ozone through insufflation in the USA.

Ozone has been found to convert cholesterol in the blood stream to plaque (which causes hardening and narrowing of arteries). This cholesterol product has also been implicated in Alzheimer's disease, suggesting a link between the inflammatory response associated with head injury and Alzheimer's.

Ozone has been studied extensively, and found to be carcinogenic to some animals (and not others), and a mutagen to some bacteria.

Ozone layer

The ozone layer is that part of the stratosphere which contains ozone. The total quantity of ozone in the ozone layer is not very large; if just the ozone were compressed to the pressure of the air at sea level, it would be only a few millimeters thick.

Ozone is notable for its ability to absorb certain wavelengths of ultraviolet radiation:

> "The stratospheric ozone layer is important because, among other things, it reduces the amount of solar ultraviolet-B radiation reaching the Earth's surface. UV-B is the main cause of basal and squamous cell skin cancers, but not of malignant melanoma; the latter is primarily caused by UV-A— which is not absorbed by ozone."

Ozone in the earth's atmosphere is generally created by ultraviolet light striking oxygen molecules containing two oxygen atoms (O_2), splitting them into individual oxygen atoms (atomic oxygen); the atomic oxygen then combines with unbroken O_2 to create ozone, O_3. The ozone molecule is also unstable and when ultraviolet light hits ozone it splits into a molecule of O_2 and an atom of atomic oxygen, a continuing process called the ozone-oxygen cycle, thus creating an ozone layer in the stratosphere.

The ozone layer can be destroyed by the presence of atomic chlorine, fluorine or bromine in the atmosphere leading to the so-called ozone hole in the polar stratosphere during winter months; these elements are found in certain stable compounds, especially chlorofluorocarbons (CFCs) which may find their way to the stratosphere and there be liberated by the action of ultraviolet light on them. All the gases mentioned are denser than air, so they eventually diffuse to ground level and there are absorbed by reacting with almost anything organic, but have plenty of time to catalyze the breakdown of ozone in the meantime. Chlorine in particular is capable of breaking down approximately one hundred thousand times its molarity of ozone.

The concentration of atmospheric ozone in the ozone layer varies by a large factor worldwide, being thicker near the equator and thinner at the poles. Ozone levels, over the northern hemisphere, are dropping by ~4% per year. Approximately ~4.6% of the Earth's surface is not covered by the ozone layer; these are the ozone holes.

On January 23, 1978 Sweden became the first nation to ban aerosol sprays that are thought to damage the ozone layer.

On August 2, 2003, scientists announced that the depletion of the ozone layer may be slowing down due to an international ban on chlorofluorocarbons. Three satellites and three ground stations confirmed that the upper atmosphere ozone depletion rate has slowed down significantly during the past decade. The study was organized by the American Geophysical Union.

Tropospheric Ozone

Ozone (O_3) in the troposphere, is a pollutant, a constituent of smog. Many highly energetic reactions produce it, ranging from combustion to photocopying. Often laser printers will have a smell of ozone, which in high concentrations is toxic. Ozone oxidises readily producing many possibly toxic oxides.

The troposphere extends to approximately 16 kilometers above the surface of the Earth and consists of many layers. Ozone is more concentrated above the mixing layer, or ground layer. Ground-level ozone, though less concentrated than ozone aloft, is more of a problem because of its health effects.

Satellites can measure tropospheric ozone. Measurements specifically of ground-level ozone require in-situ monitoring with 2004 technology.

Formation

The majority of tropospheric ozone is formed when nitrogen oxides (NO_x) and volatile organic compounds (VOCs), such as xylene, react in the atmosphere in the presence of sunlight. NO_x and VOCs are called ozone precursors. Motor vehicle exhaust, industrial emissions, and chemical solvents are the major sources of these chemicals. Although these precursors often originate in urban areas, winds can carry NO_x hundreds of kilometers, causing ozone formation to occur in less populated regions as well.

Health effects

Ozone can irritate the respiratory system, causing coughing, throat irritation, and/or an uncomfortable sensation in the chest.

Ozone can reduce lung function and make it more difficult to breathe deeply and vigorously. Breathing may become more rapid and shallow than normal. This may limit a person's ability to engage in vigorous activities.

Ozone can aggravate asthma. When ozone levels are high, more people with asthma have attacks that require a doctor's attention or use of medication. One reason this happens is that ozone makes people more sensitive to allergens, the most common triggers of asthma attacks. Ozone can increase susceptibility to respiratory infections.

Ozone can inflame and damage the lining of the lungs. Within a few days, the damaged cells are shed and replaced much like the skin peels after a sunburn. Animal studies suggest that if this type of inflammation happens repeatedly over a long time period (months, years, a lifetime), lung tissue may become permanently scarred, resulting in permanent loss of lung function, and a lower quality of life.

CHLOROFLUOROCARBONS

CFCs (chlorofluorocarbons) are a family of artificial chemical compounds containing chlorine, fluorine and carbon. They were formerly used widely in industry, for example as refrigerants, propellants and cleaning solvents. Their use has been generally prohibited by the Montreal Protocol, because of fears of their possible destructive effects on the ozone layer. Hydrochlorofluorocarbons are now used as CFC substitutes.

CFCs were developed by the American engineer Thomas Midgley in 1928 as a replacement for ammonia (then a common refrigerant). The new compound developed had to have a low boiling point, a lack of toxicity and be generally non-reactive. In a demonstration for the American Chemical Association, Midgley flamboyantly demonstrated all these properties by inhaling a breath of the gas and using it to blow out a candle.

Midgley specifically developed CCl_2F_2 (CFC-12). However one of the attractive features of CFCs is that there exists a whole family of the compounds, each having a unique boiling point which can suit different applications. As well as refrigerants, CFCs have been used as propellants in aerosol cans, cleaning solvents for circuit boards, and as blowing agents for making expanded plastics (such as those once used to store fast-foods.)

There has been a movement since the late 1970s to ban CFCs because of their destructive effect on the ozone layer. This damage was discovered due mainly to the work of scientists Sherry Rowland and Mario Molina, first published in 1974. It turns out that one of CFCs most attractive features - its unreactivity - has been instrumental in making it one of our worst pollutants. CFC's lack of reactivity gives it a lifespan which can exceed 100 years in some cases. This gives it time to diffuse up in to the upper stratosphere. Here the sun's UV radiation is strong enough to break off the chlorine atom, which on its own is a highly reactive free radical. This catalyses the break up of ozone in to oxygen:

$$Cl + O_3 \rightarrow ClO + O_2$$

$$ClO + O \rightarrow Cl + O_2$$

CFCs are a problem because the chlorine is regenerated at the end of these reactions, making it able to keep on reacting with millions of other ozone molecules. The ozone hole produced is able to let through UV light, which increases the chances of cancer in humans.

In 1985, scientists documented a drastic depletion of the ozone layer over Antarctica which lead the United Nations to take action in 1987. International attention to CFCs resulted in a meeting of UN diplomats from around the world in Montreal in 1987. They forged a treaty that called for drastic reductions in the production of CFCs. On March 2, 1989 12 European Community nations agreed to ban the production of all CFCs by the end century. In 1990, diplomats met in London and voted to significantly strengthen the Montreal Protocol by calling for a complete elimination of CFCs by the year 2000. by the year 2010 CFCs should be completely eliminated from developing countries as well.

One major use of CFCs has been as propellants in aerosol inhalers for drugs used to treat asthma. The conversion of these devices and treatments from CFC to halocarbons that do not have the same effect on the ozone layer is well under way. There are some differences between asthma inhalers using CFCs and the newer propellants, but in general conversion is easy.

CFCs HCFCs and HFCs are named as follows:

CFC-01234a, where:

— 0 = number of double bonds (omitted if zero)

— 1 = Carbon atoms - 1 (omitted if zero)

— 2 = Hydrogen atoms + 1

— 3 = Fluorine atoms

— 4 = Chlorine atoms replaced by Bromine ("B" prefix added)

— a = letter added to identify isomers, the "normal" isomer in any number has the smallest mass difference on each carbon, and a, b, or c are added as the masses diverge from normal.

Examples:

Short name	Formula	Full name
CFC-12	CCl_2F_2	dichlorodifluoromethane
HCFC-22	$CHClF_2$	chlorodifluoromethane
HFC-134	CHF_2-CHF_2	1,1,2,2-tetrafluoroethane
HFC-134a	CH_2F-CF_3	1,2,2,2-tetrafluoroethane

Increasing Level of CFC in Environment

For over 50 years, chlorofluorocarbons (CFCs) were thought of as miracle substances. They are stable, nonflammable, low in toxicity, and inexpensive to produce. Over time, CFCs found uses as refrigerants, solvents, foam blowing agents, and in other smaller applications. Other chlorine-containing compounds include methyl chloroform, a solvent, and carbon tetrachloride, an industrial chemical. Halons, extremely effective fire extinguishing agents, and methyl bromide, an effective produce and soil fumigant, contain bromine.

All of these compounds have atmospheric lifetimes long enough to allow them to be transported by winds into the stratosphere. Because they release chlorine or bromine when they break down, they damage the protective ozone layer. The discussion of the ozone depletion process below focuses on CFCs, but the basic concepts apply to all of the ozone-depleting substances (ODS).

In the early 1970s, researchers began to investigate the effects of various chemicals on the ozone layer, particularly CFCs, which contain chlorine. They also examined the potential impacts of other chlorine sources. Chlorine from swimming pools, industrial plants, sea salt, and volcanoes does not reach the stratosphere. Chlorine compounds from these sources readily combine with water and repeated measurements show that they rain out of the troposphere very quickly. In contrast, CFCs are very stable and do not dissolve in rain. Thus, there are no natural processes that remove the CFCs from the lower atmosphere. Over time, winds drive the CFCs into the stratosphere.

The CFCs are so stable that only exposure to strong UV radiation breaks them down. When that happens, the CFC molecule releases atomic chlorine. One chlorine atom can destroy over 100,000 ozone molecules. The net effect is to destroy ozone faster than it is naturally created. To return to the analogy comparing ozone levels to a stream's depth, CFCs act as a siphon, removing water faster than normal and reducing the depth of the stream.

Large fires and certain types of marine life produce one stable form of chlorine that does reach the stratosphere. However, numerous experiments have shown that CFCs and other widely-used chemicals produce roughly 85% of the chlorine in the stratosphere, while natural sources contribute only 15%.

Large volcanic eruptions can have an indirect effect on ozone levels. Although Mt. Pinatubo's 1991 eruption did not increase stratospheric chlorine concentrations, it did produce large amounts of tiny particles called aerosols (different from consumer products also known as aerosols). These aerosols increase chlorine's effectiveness at destroying ozone.

The aerosols only increased depletion because of the presence of CFC- based chlorine. In effect, the aerosols increased the efficiency of the CFC siphon, lowering ozone levels even more than would have otherwise occurred. Unlike long-term ozone depletion, however, this effect is short-lived. The aerosols from Mt. Pinatubo have already disappeared, but satellite, ground-based, and balloon data still show ozone depletion occurring closer to the historic trend. One example of ozone depletion is the annual ozone "hole" over Antarctica that has occurred during the Antarctic Spring since the early 1980s. Rather than being a literal hole through the layer, the ozone hole is a large area of the stratosphere with extremely low amounts of ozone. Ozone levels fall by over 60% during the worst years. In addition, research has shown that ozone depletion occurs over the latitudes that include North America, Europe, Asia, and much of Africa, Australia, and South America. Over the U.S., ozone levels have fallen 5-10%, depending on the season. Thus, ozone depletion is a global issue and not just a problem at the South Pole.

Reductions in ozone levels will lead to higher levels of UVB reaching the Earth's surface. The sun's output of UVB does not change; rather, less ozone means less protection, and hence more UVB reaches the Earth. Studies have shown that in the Antarctic, the amount of UVB measured at the surface can double during the annual ozone hole. Another study confirmed the relationship between reduced ozone and increased UVB levels in Canada during the past several years.

Laboratory and epidemiological studies demonstrate that UVB causes nonmelanoma skin cancer and plays a major role in malignant melanoma development. In addition, UVB has been linked to cataracts. All sunlight contains some UVB, even with normal ozone levels. It is always important to limit exposure to the sun. However, ozone depletion will increase the amount of UVB, which will then increase the risk of health effects. Furthermore, UVB harms some crops, plastics and other materials, and certain types of marine life.

OZONE DEPLETION

Image of the largest antarctic ozone hole ever recorded in September 2000. Data taken by the Total Ozone Mapping Spectrometer (TOMS) instrument aboard NASA's Earth Probe satellite.

Ozone depletion refers to reductions in the amount of ozone in the stratosphere. There was a reduction of approximately 5% detected from 1979 to 1990.

The ozone hole refers to annual, temporary reductions in the polar regions, where much larger losses in ozone occur each spring - up to 70% over Antarctica or 30% over the Arctic — followed by recovery in the summer. This reduction is held by a wide scientific consensus to be due primarily to an increase in concentrations of stratospheric chlorine from breakdown of human manufactured CFC emissions. Ozone depletion varies geographically and by season.

Since the ozone layer prevents most harmful wavelengths of ultraviolet light from passing through the earth's atmosphere, observed and projected decreases in ozone have generated worldwide concern and led to speedy adoption of the Montreal Protocol banning CFC use.

In public policy discussions, the term *ozone layer depletion* is considered synonymous with the theory that a trend of global ozone depletion, which is caused by CFC emissions, is subsequently allowing more ultraviolet radiation to reach the earth's surface. It is suspected that a variety of biological consequences, including, for example, increases in melanoma and the destruction of plankton populations in the ocean's photic zone, may result from this increased UV exposure.

History of the research

In 1970 Prof. Paul Crutzen pointed out the possibility that nitrogen oxides from fertilizers and supersonic aircraft might deplete the ozone layer. In 1974 Frank Sherwood Rowland and Mario J. Molina realised that when CFCs finally break apart in the atmosphere and release chlorine atoms they cause ozone depletion. These three scientists received the Nobel Prize in Chemistry in 1995 for this work. They calculated that if CFC production continued to increase at the going rate of 10%/year until 1990, then remain steady, CFCs would cause a global 5 to 7 percent ozone loss by 1995 and 30-50% loss by 2050. However, the discovery of the Antarctic "ozone hole" by Farman, Gardiner and Shanklin was a surprise - chemical reactions on PSCs in the cold Antarctic stratosphere caused faster depletion than expected - and caused worldwide publicity.

Satellite measurements showing massive depletion of ozone around the south pole were becoming available at the same time. However, these were initially rejected as unreasonable by data quality control algorithms; the ozone hole was only detected in satellite data when the raw data was reprocessed following evidence of an ozone hole in *in situ* observations.

Ozone depletion has been observed all over the globe but is greatest at high latitudes (that is, near the poles). The best known example is the annual thinning of the ozone layer over Antarctica during the polar spring.

Since 1981 the UNEP has sponsored a series of reports on scientific assessment of ozone depletion. The most recent is from 2002.

Causes

Releasing CFCs into the atmosphere has caused ozone depletion. Since the ozone layer absorbs UV, this would be expected to increase surface UV levels, which could lead to damage, including increases in skin cancer. This is the reason for the Montreal Protocol on Substances that Deplete the Ozone Layer. Although decreases in stratospheric ozone are well-tied to CFC's, and there are good theoretical reasons to believe that decreases in ozone will lead to increases in surface UV, there is not much direct observational evidence linking ozone depletion to additional skin cancer in human beings.

Ozone in the Earth's atmosphere is generally created by ultraviolet light striking oxygen molecules, which consist of two oxygen atoms (O_2), creating two single oxygen atoms, known as atomic oxygen. The atomic oxygen then combines with a molecule of O_2 to create ozone, O_3.

The ozone molecule is also unstable and when hit by ultraviolet light it splits into a molecule of O_2 and an atom of atomic oxygen, a continuing process called the ozone-oxygen cycle. Ozone can be destroyed by atomic chlorine, fluorine or bromine in the atmosphere. These elements are found in certain stable compounds, especially chlorofluorocarbons (CFCs), which may find their way to the stratosphere and there be liberated by the action of ultraviolet light.

Most importantly, the chlorine atoms so generated destroy ozone molecules in a catalytic cycle. In this cycle a single chlorine atom would keep on destroying ozone forever, were it not for reactions that remove chlorine atoms from this cycle by forming reservoir species such as hydrochloric acid and chlorine nitrate. The reactivation of atomic chlorine from these reservoir species is normally slow, but is enhanced by the presence of polar stratospheric clouds which appear during Antarctic winters, leading to a strong seasonal cycle in ozone hole formation.

The importance of the reaction on polar stratospheric cloud is many-fold. The PSC's only form in extreme cold; the Antarctic stratosphere is colder than the Arctic; which is why ozone holes first formed over Antarctica and why the Arctic ones are not as deep. The original predictions failed to take into account PCS's, which is why a sudden Antarctic ozone hole, rather than gradual global depletion, was such a surprise.

Ozone depletion also explains much of the the observed reduction in stratospheric and upper tropospheric temperatures. This is because the reason for the warmth of the stratosphere is absorption of UV radiation by ozone, hence reduced ozone leads to cooling. Some stratospheric cooling is also predicted from increases in greenhouse gases such as CO_2; however the ozone-induced cooling is found to be probably dominant.

Predictions of ozone remains a difficult science. The World Meteorological Organization Global Ozone Research and Monitoring Project - Report No. 44, which on balance comes out strongly in favour of the Montreal protocol, nonetheless notes that projections of ozone loss for the 1994-1997 period made in the UNEP 1994 Assessment had been an overestimate.

Observations

The most pronounced decrease in ozone has been in the lower stratosphere. However, the ozone hole is most usually measured not in terms of ozone concentrations at these levels (which are typically of a few parts per million) but by reduction in the total *column ozone*, above a point on the earth's surface, which is normally expressed in Dobson units. Marked decreases in column ozone in the antarctic spring and early summer compared to the early 1970s and before have been observed using instruments such as the Total Ozone Mapping Spectrometer (TOMS).

Substantial reductions of up to 70% in the ozone column observed in the austral (i.e. southern hemispheric) spring over Antarctica and first reported in 1985 are continuing. Through the 1990's, total column ozone in September and October have continued to be 40-50% lower than pre-ozone-hole values. In the arctic, declines are greatest in winter/spring and the amount is more variable year-to-year than in the Antarctic: when the stratosphere is colder the losses are greater, up to 30%

In mid latitudes it is probably preferable to speak of ozone depletion rather than holes; declines are about 3% below pre-1980 values for 35-60N and about 6% for 35-60S. In the tropics, there are no significant trends.

The ozone hole and its causes

The cause of the ozone holes is generally agreed to be CFC (Chlorofluorocarbon) compounds which break down (due to ultraviolet light) and become free radicals containing chlorine high in the Earth's atmosphere. These radicals then break down the ozone catalytically. Ozone destruction due to chlorine radicals from CFCs can take place in the gas phase, but occurs particularly rapidly on the surface of polar stratospheric clouds (PSC), which form over the poles (particularly the south pole) during winter. A rise in CFC production has accompanied the ozone depletion and a plausible chemical mechanism for CFC's role in ozone depletion has been proposed. As a result, a worldwide ban on most uses of CFCs, the Montreal Protocol, was signed and entered into force in 1989.

The photochemical processes involved are complex but well understood, with UV radiation being involved in both the natural production and destruction of ozone, as well as the breakdown of CFCs into free radicals and the destruction of ozone by chlorine radicals. The role of sunlight in ozone depletion is the reason why the Antarctic ozone depletion is greatest during spring; during winter, even though PSCs are at their most abundant, there is no light over the pole to drive the chemical reactions.

CFCs are a byproduct of some chemical processes, and were also used in air conditioning/cooling units. They were also widely used as aerosol propellants prior to the 1980s. What makes CFCs so effective in breaking down ozone is that one CFC radical acts as a catalyst and can break down many ozone molecules. Furthermore, these radicals stay in the atmosphere for a very long time.

Scientists have increasingly been able to attribute the observed ozone depletion to the increase of anthropogenic halogen compounds from CFCs, by the use of complex chemical transport models and their validation against observational data. These models work by combining satellite measurements of chemical concentrations and meteorological fields with chemical reaction rate constants obtained in lab experiments, and are able to identify not only the key chemical reactions but also the transport processes which bring CFC photolysis products into contact with ozone.

Increased UV due to the ozone hole

Although ozone, O_3, is a minority constituent in the earth's atmosphere, it is responsible for most of the main absorption of ultraviolet (UV) radiation in the atmosphere. Correspondingly, a significant decrease in atmospheric ozone could be expected to give rise to significantly increased levels of UV near the surface.

Increases in surface UV due to the ozone hole can be partially inferred by radiative transfer model calculations, but cannot be calculated from direct measurements because of the lack of reliable historical (pre-ozone-hole) surface UV data, although more recent surface UV observation measurement programmes exist.

Because it is this same UV radiation that creates the ozone in the ozone layer from O_2 (regular oxygen) in the first place, a reduction in stratospheric ozone would actually tend to increase photochemical production of ozone at lower levels (in the troposphere), although the overall observed trends in total column ozone are still a decrease, largely because ozone produced lower down has a naturally shorter photochemical lifetime, so it is destroyed before the concentrations could reach a level which would compensate for the ozone reduction higher up.

Biological effects of increased UV

The main public concern regarding the ozone hole has been the effects of surface UV on human health. As the ozone hole over Antarctica has in some instances grown so large as to reach southern parts of Australia and New Zealand, environmentalists have been concerned that the increase in surface UV could be significant.

UVB (the higher energy UV radiation absorbed by ozone) is generally accepted to be a contributory factor to malignant melanoma (skin cancer) — for example one study showed that a 10% increase in the UVB was associated with a 19% increase in melanomas for men and 16% for women

So far, ozone depletion in most locations has been typically a few percent. Were the high levels of depletion seen in the ozone hole ever to be common across the globe, the effects could be substantially more dramatic. For example, recent research has analyzed a widespread extinction of plankton 2 million years ago that coincided with a nearby supernova. Researchers speculate that the extinction was caused by a significant weakening of the ozone layer at that time when the radiation from the supernova produced nitrogen oxides that catalyzed the destruction of ozone (plankton are particularly susceptible to effects of UV light, and are vitally important to marine food-webs).

Aside from the direct effect of ultraviolet radiation on organisms, increased surface UV leads to increased tropospheric ozone, as noted above. Paradoxically, at ground-level *increased* ozone is generally recognised to be a health risk, as ozone is toxic due to its strong oxidant properties.

Public policy in response to the ozone hole

Environmentalists assert that the CFCs have caused so much damage to the ozone layer that the use of CFCs should be banned. The full extent of this damage CFCs have caused is not known and will not be known for decades; however marked decreases in column ozone have already been observed.

In 1987, the Montreal Protocol was signed, controlling the emissions of CFCs. To some extent, their role has been replaced by the less damaging hydro-chloro-fluoro-carbons (HCFCs), although concerns remain regarding HCFCs also.

The future of ozone depletion

Since the adoption and strengthening of the Montreal Protocol has lead to reductions in the emissions of CFC's, etc, the atmospheric concentrations of these compounds has begun to stabilize and in some cases decline. In the long term these substance will be gradually removed from the atmosphere and by 2050 ozone holes should have declined.

There is a slight caveat to this, however. Global warming from CO_2 radiative forcing is expected (perhaps somewhat surprisingly) to cool the stratosphere. This, in turn, would lead to a relative increase in ozone depletion and the frequency of ozone holes. The effect may not be linear: ozone holes form because of polar stratospheric cloud; the formation of polar stratospheric clouds has a temperature threshold above which they will not form; cooling of the Arctic stratosphere might lead to Antarctic-ozone-hole-like conditions. But at the moment this is not clear.

Controversy regarding ozone science and policy

Any counter-measures which have a negative economic impact will remain a controversial issue due to the strong economic interests involved, with key questions regarding whether the scientific understanding is strong enough to warrant the proposed countermeasures. In this context it is worth noting that it is commonly believed that one reason for the relative ease of introduction of the Montreal protocol was the availability of CFC replacements at little extra cost.

The consensus amongst most atmospheric physicists and chemists is that the scientific understanding has now reached a level where countermeasures to control CFC emissions are justified, although the decision is ultimately one for policy-makers and society.

Some atmospheric scientists (for instance Fred Singer, founder of SEPP and also a global warming skeptic) and industry-sponsored advocacy groups question or completely deny a link between CFCs and ozone depletion. It is common to see completely nonsensical arguments put forward to prove that CFCs cannot cause ozone depletion - for example, that they are heavier than air and so cannot reach the stratosphere.

CFCs are heavier than air, but just like argon, krypton and other heavy gases with a long lifetime they are uniformly distributed throughout the turbosphere and reach the upper atmosphere.

Despite this general consensus, the science behind ozone depletion remains complex, and some who oppose the enforcement of countermeasures point to some of the difficulties experienced in these studies. For example:

Although increased UVB has been shown to constitute a melanoma risk, it has been difficult for statistical studies to establish a direct link between ozone depletion and increased rates of melanoma. Although melanomas did increase significantly during the period 1970-1990, it is difficult to separate reliably the effect of ozone depletion from the effect of changes in lifestyle factors.

CLIMATE CHANGE

The term climate change is used to refer to changes in the Earth's climate. Generally, this is taken to mean changes in the temperature, though 'climate' encompasses many other variables (precipitation, clouds, etc). 'Climate change' can be caused both by natural forces and by human activities; 'global warming' is usually used to mean changes with predominantly human causes. For information on climate change over various periods, and the data sources available.

There is general agreement among scientists (as revealed by the scientific literature) that:

— The 100 kyr ice age cycles are controlled by orbital forcing -variations in the seasonal and geographical distribution of insolation; and in the total insolation.

— The rapid temperature changes seen in ice cores during the last glacial were probably caused by events associated with the Laurentide ice sheet and thus count as "internal variability".

— The Little Ice Age was probably caused by solar variation or volcanic activity.

Climate change factors

Climate changes due to *internal factors* and *external factors*. Internal factors are those due to interactions within the earth's climate system. External factors are divided into natural factors, such as variations in solar radiation, and anthropogenic factors (those attributed to human activities).

Internal factors

It is known that the weather is a chaotic non-linear dynamical system. It is not clear that the climate (the average of weather) is such a system. Restricting ourselves to the last 400 kyr, the ice core record shows that the largest swings in climate are periodic, with the same periodicity as various orbital variations. These are thus non-chaotic. However, there are large short-term changes which do seem to be best explained as chaotic. Those variations do not seem to occur in the current climate state. Thus, it is possible that the climate system varies between chaotic and non-chaotic, depending on the state of the external forcing.

Natural Factors

It is clear that natural external factors have caused significant climate changes in the past, and it is probable that internal factors have too.

Human Factors

Anthropogenic factors are acts by humans (Homo sapiens) that change the environment and influence the climate. The major factor is CO_2 emission from fossil fuel combustion. Other factors include forest alterations, and agricultural or other changes that affect the Earth's albedo, the carbon cycle, or methane production.

Solar Radiation Variability

The main natural external factor is the variability in the amount, and geographic and temporal distribution of, solar radiation that reaches Earth. The solar radiation can change on short (yearly to century) timescales because of solar cycles and on century to millennial timescales because of cyclic changes in Earth's orbit. On much longer (hundreds of millions of years) timescales, the Sun is getting hotter.

Examples of change due to natural factors

The 100,000 year ice age cycles are due to natural causes. Within the last 1000 years, there are two extensive periods where temperatures were relatively warmer (the Medieval Warm Period) or cooler (the Little Ice Age). Since anthropogenic forcing is believed to have been small then, it is assumed that these changes were due to natural factors. The Little Ice Age is usually attributed to the reduction ot solar activity or increase in volcanoes; the causes of the MWP are even less clear.

A few scientists have claimed that the observed warming since 1860 is a natural climate recovery from the Little Ice Age.

Anthropogenic greenhouse gases

The main anthropogenic factors are greenhouse gases, whose increased emissions add to the greenhouse effect; changes in land use; and the emission of aerosols such as sulphates. Large amounts of anthropogenic greenhouse gases have been emitted to the atmosphere since the beginning of the industrial revolution. Since 1750: the carbon dioxide concentration has increased by 31%, methane has increased 151%, nitrous oxide has increased 17% and tropospheric ozone has increased 36%.

The majority of the anthropogenic carbon dioxide is produced by the combustion of fossil fuels. Methane is produced by cattle, energy, and rice production in similar amounts, each of which emit about 66% of the amount produced by the major natural source, wetlands.

Carbon Sources and Sinks

Forests which are regrowing in North America and Russia contribute to absorbing carbon dioxide (they act as CO_2 sinks), and since 1990, the amount of carbon absorbed may be larger than the amount released by deforestation. Conversely, deforestation largely in tropical countries is a source of CO_2 to the atmosphere. CO_2 releases from deforestation are probably about 1/6 of sources from fossil fuel conbustion.

Not all the CO_2 emitted to the atmosphere accumulates there; half of it is absorbed, presumably by oceans and forests, as a modification to the natural carbon cycle.

Evaluation of the relative importance of various factors

The relative importance of each of the proposed causes varies according to the period of interest: for example, anthropogenic factors are presumed to be negligibly small for climate change before, say, 1750. However, this has recently been challenged by Ruddiman who claims that ancient forest clearance and rice paddies increased CO_2 and methane levels starting 8000 years ago. Otherwise, their importance can be established through the quantification of the factors involved. Internal factors and the response to external factors can be estimated by the analysis of climate simulations based on the best climate models.

MONTREAL PROTOCOL ON SUBSTANCES THAT DEPLETE THE OZONE LAYER

The Montreal Protocol on Substances That Deplete the Ozone Layer is an international treaty designed to protect the ozone layer from depletion by phasing out the production of a number of substances believed to be responsible for ozone depletion. The treaty was opened for signature on September 16, 1987 and entered into force on January 1, 1989. Since then, it has undergone five revisions, in 1990 (London), 1992 (Copenhagen), 1995 (Vienna), 1997 (Montreal), and 1999 (Beijing). Due to its widespread adoption and adhearance it has been hailed as an example of exceptional international cooperation with Kofi Annan quoted as saying it is "Perhaps the single most successful international agreement to date..."

Terms and purpose

The treaty is structured around several groups of halogenated hydrocarbons that have been implicated to play a role in ozone depletion. For each group, the treaty provides a timetable on which the production of those substances must be phased out and eventually eliminated.

The stated purpose of the treaty is that the signatory states:

> ...Recognizing that world-wide emissions of certain substances can significantly deplete and otherwise modify the ozone layer in a manner that is likely to result in adverse effects on human health and the environment, ... Determined to protect the ozone layer by taking precautionary measures to control equitably total global emissions of substances that deplete it, with the ultimate objective of their elimination on the basis of developments in scientific knowledge ... Acknowledging that special provision is required to meet the needs of developing countries...

shall accept a series of stepped limits on CFC use, and production, including:

— from 1991 to 1992 its levels of consumption and production of the controlled substances in Group I of Annex A do not exceed 150 per cent of its calculated levels of production and consumption of those substances in 1986;

— from 1994 its calculated level of consumption and production of the controlled substances in Group I of Annex A does not exceed, annually, twenty-five per cent of its calculated level of consumption and production in 1986.

— from 1996 its calculated level of consumption and production of the controlled substances in Group I of Annex A does not exceed zero.

There is a slower phase-out (to zero by 2010) of other substances (halon 1211, 1301, 2402; cfc's 13, 111, 112, etc) and some chemicals get individual attention (Carbon tetrachloride; Methyl chloroform).

The substances in Group I of Annex A are:

— $CFCl_3$ (CFC-11)

— CF_2Cl_2 (CFC-12)

— $C_2F_3C_{13}$ (CFC-113)

— $C_2F_4Cl_2$(CFC-114)

— C_2F_5Cl (CFC-115)

Science

The provisions of the Protocol include the requirement that the Parties to the Protocol base their future decisions on the current scientific, environmental, technical, and economic information that is assessed through panels drawn from the worldwide expert communities. To provide that input to the decision-making process, advances in understanding on these topics were assessed in 1989, 1991, 1994, 1998 and 2002 in a series of reports entitled Scientific assessment of ozone depletion.

SCIENTIFIC ASSESSMENT OF OZONE DEPLETION

Scientific Assessment of Ozone Depletion is a sequence of reports sponsored by WMO/UNEP. The most recent is the 2002 report. The reports were set up to inform the Montreal Protocol and amendments about ozone depletion.

Findings

Changes in Ozone-Depleting Compounds

— In the troposphere observations show that the total abundance of ozone-depleting compounds continues to decline slowly from the peak that occurred in 1992-1994.

— Observations in the stratosphere indicate that the total chlorine abundance is at or near a peak, while bromine abundances are probably still increasing.

— Analyses of air trapped in snow since the late 19th century have confirmed that non-industrial sources of the CFCs, halons, and major chlorocarbons were insignificant.

— The abundances of HCFCs in the troposphere continue to increase.

Changes in the Ozone Layer over the Poles and Globally

— Springtime Antarctic ozone depletion due to halogens has been large (40-50%; exceptionally 70%) throughout the last decade.

— In some recent cold Arctic winters during the last decade, maximum total column ozone losses due to halogens have reached 30%, but in warmer winters Arctic ozone loss is small.

— Ozone remains depleted in the midlatitudes of both hemispheres. The global-average total column ozone amount for the period 1997-2001 was approximately 3% below the pre-1980 average values.

— Models capture the observed long-term ozone changes in northern and southern midlatitudes.

Changes in Ultraviolet Radiation

Decreases in ozone amounts lead to increases in UV radiation. Calculations of UV irradiance based on relationships with total ozone and total irradiance suggest that UV irradiance has increased since the early 1980s by 6-14% at more than 10 sites distributed over mid- and high latitudes of both hemispheres. But complexities (e.g. clouds, aerosol, snow cover, sea ice cover, and total ozone) limit the ability to describe fully surface ultraviolet radiation on the global scale. Surface ultraviolet data records, which started in the early 1990s, are still too short and too variable to permit the calculation of statistically significant long-term (i.e., multidecadal) trends.

Predictions

— Chemistry-climate models predict that springtime Antarctic ozone levels will be increasing by 2010 because of projected decreases of halogens in the stratosphere. A return to pre-1980 total column ozone amounts in the Antarctic is expected by the middle of this century.

— Arctic ozone depletion is highly variable and difficult to predict, but a future Arctic polar ozone hole similar to that of the Antarctic appears unlikely.

6

Environmental Awareness through Education

Environmental degradation is a serious issue in the world today. Human factor is the largest contributor to the environmental degradation. Zoos and aquariums have the potential to raise environmental awareness and generate community involvement through conservation education.

Today, the world is facing environmental degradation. Green house effect has changed the global climate. Ecosystem damage and pollution have decreased the biodiversity. The condition in Indonesia is very serious. Human impact is the biggest reason for environmental degradation, by doing such activities:

— Natural resources over exploitation

— Changes of land use

— Increase in pollution and utilization of dangerous chemical compounds

— Bombing and cyanide fishing, coral mining

— Sedimentation

— Tourism activities

To increase the people's awareness of the importance environmental protection and to enable them to participate in the efforts of environmental conservation, governments must implement environmental education and awareness programmes.

Environmental education is a learning process that increases knowledge and awareness about the environment and develops skills that enable responsible decisions and actions that impact the environment. Environmental education encourages inquiry and investigation and enables the learner to develop critical-thinking, problem-solving, and effective decision-making skills. Environmental education enables individuals to weigh various sides of an environmental issue. It does not advocate a particular viewpoint or course of action.

PRIORITY OF ENVIRONMENTAL EDUCATION IN THE 21ST CENTURY

Education in all its forms is essential to sustainable development. In many respects primary education makes a positive contribution to combating the problems of poverty, the degradation of the environment and the improvement of nutrition. Improved access to primary education for girls and women yields tangible benefits, including reductions in birth rates and improvements in health. Education is also an important factor in fostering social cohesion and democratic government.

Scientific education has a unique part to play in facilitating sustainable development because it can widen our capacities, especially in areas such as eco-technology and the development of renewable energy sources, and it can ensure the widespread availability of scientific information, which in turn is increasingly necessary for informed ethical decision-making.

Education not only provides the scientific and technical skills required, it also provides the motivation, justification, and social support for pursuing and applying them. Education increases the capacities of people to transform their visions of society into operational realities. It is for this reason that education is the primary agent of transformation towards sustainable development. It is also for this reason that society must be deeply concerned that much of the education presently on offer falls far short of what is required. Improving the quality and coverage of education and reorienting its goals to recognize the importance of sustainable development must be among society's highest priorities.

It is widely agreed that education is the most effective means that society possesses for confronting the challenges of the future. Indeed, education will shape the world of tomorrow. Progress increasingly depends upon the products of educated minds: upon research, invention, innovation and adaptation. Of course, educated minds and instincts are needed not only in laboratories and research institutes, but in every walk of life. Indeed, access to education is the sine qua non for effective participation in the life of the modern world at all levels. Education, to be certain, is not the whole answer to every problem. But education, in its broadest sense, must be a vital part of all efforts to imagine and create new relations among people and to foster greater respect for the needs of the environment.

Over time, education also powerfully affects cultures and societies, increasing their concern over unsustainable practices and their capacities to confront and master change. The potential of education is enormous. Not only it can inform people, but it can change them. It is not only a means for personal enlightenment, but also for cultural renewal.

Education serves society in a variety of ways. The goal of education is to make people wiser, more knowledgeable, better informed, ethical, responsible, critical and capable of continuing to learn. Were all people to possess such abilities and qualities, the world's problems would not be automatically solved, but the means and the will to address them would be at hand. Education also serves society by providing a critical reflection on the world, especially its failings and injustices, and by promoting greater consciousness and awareness, exploring new visions and concepts, and inventing new techniques and tools. Education is also the means for disseminating knowledge and developing skills, for bringing about desired changes in behaviours, values and lifestyles, and for promoting public support for the continuing and fundamental changes that will be required. Education is humanity's best hope and most effective means in the quest to achieve sustainable development.

Education is considered as the essential foundation for sustainable development and as indispensable for advances in other spheres, such as sciences, technology, legislation and production. Education is no longer seen as an end in itself, but as a means:

— To effect the changes in value systems, behavioural patterns and lifestyles necessary to achieve sustainable development, and ultimately democracy, security and peace.

— To disseminate the knowledge and skills necessary to foster sustainable production and consumption patterns and to improve the management of natural resources, agriculture, energy and industrial production.

— To ensure an informed populace, prepared to support changes in other sectors conducive to sustainability.

Global and local environmental issues are becoming severer year by year, which you may find by considering many phenomena, which are considered to be attributed by climate change and other origins. Mary of the causes of them are considered at the results from human activities. From these facts, it is important for children to know about those phenomena themselves and also about the reasons, as well as about how to respond by themselves. It is also important for human to have concepts of working together, locally and globally. This can be understood by considering about the fact that one country cannot stop the increase of green house gases on the earth to stop the global warming.

Considering from those, the environmental education for children should contain at least following items:

— To develop the sensitivity of children to feel good or bad environment, which leads to development of environmental awareness of children

— To understand the mechanism of the nature and its sustainability

— To understand the impact of human activity of the nature

— To learn about how to manage the human activity to reduce its impact

— To make practice to work together locally and globally to reduce the impact of human on nature

REQUIRED EDUCATION REFORMS

"Education reform" means different things to different people. But the one thing that all "reformers" agree on is that the goal of education reform is to improve learning. Many advocates of education reform are stressing the need to use new approaches to teaching and learning that involve changes in curriculum and instruction. Others are calling for the need for more fundamental changes at the school site and greater accountability and assessment of progress in improving learning. The following are some examples of specific changes reformers are calling for and suggestions about how environmental education can be used as a vehicle to advance these reform goals. For example, reformers are calling for the need to:

— Provide a real world context for learning and linking the classroom to the needs of the community

 — Environmental education teaches about real issues that impact every community such as drinking water quality, indoor and outdoor air quality, habitat improvement, pesticide use and exposure, lead paint poisoning, as well as solid and hazardous waste management.

— Move away from textbook-driven, teacher-led instruction by using "hands-on," learner-centered, and cooperative learning approaches where students are actively engaged in their own learning process

  — Environmental education engages the learner in a hands-on, student-driven investigative learning process. Learners could collect and scientifically analyze air samples from their community or water samples from a local stream to assess indicators of air or water quality.

— Focus on the need to develop the learner's critical-thinking, problem-solving, and decisionmaking skills

  — Environmental education enables the learner to develop critical-thinking, problem-solving, and decision-making skills. Teams of students could investigate the availability and viability of various local modes of transportation as alternatives to single-occupancy, privately-operated vehicles and develop a plan for improving citizen choice in local transportation issues.

— Replace the traditional, compartmentalized academic subjects with an interdisciplinary curriculum that more authentically connects fields of knowledge

  — Environmental education uses an interdisciplinary curriculum that connects various academic subjects. Students could use an interdisciplinary municipal solid waste curriculum which includes activities that teach about scientific inquiry, solve mathematical problems, promote understanding of the history of local land uses, and improve writing and other communication skills.

When should environmental education begin - in the third grade? first grade? kindergarten? The answer is — even earlier. Environmental education based on life experiences should begin during the very earliest years of life. Such experiences play a critical role in shaping lifelong attitudes, values, and patterns of behavior toward natural environments.

Because young children learn about the environment by interacting with it, educators and other adults must attend to the frequency, nature, and quality of child-environment interactions during the early years. Many young children have limited opportunities for these experiences. In fact, regardless of where they live, young children spend most of their time in settings or doing activities that keep them essentially isolated from the natural world.

Recreation tends to be indoors (such as watching TV); transportation tends to be by car or other motor vehicle rather than walking; and day care programs — where many children spend most of their waking hours — tend to be oriented more toward the classroom than the outdoors. The result is that many young children are at risk of never developing positive attitudes and feelings toward the natural environment or never achieving a healthy degree of familiarity with their environment. Attention to environmental education at the early childhood level is a partial antidote to this concern.

ENVIRONMENTAL EDUCATION IN EARLY CHILDHOOD YEARS

The rationale for environmental education during the early childhood years is based on two major premises. First, children must develop a sense of respect and caring for the natural environment during their first few years of life or be at risk for never developing such attitudes. Second, positive interactions with the natural environment are an important part of healthy child development, and these interactions enhance learning and the quality of life over the span of one's lifetime.

Children who are close to nature relate to it as a source of wonder, joy, and awe. Wonder — rather than books, words, or learning all the facts — provides the direction and impetus for environmental education in early childhood. Environmental education during the early years should be based on this sense of wonder and the joy of discovery.

The following guidelines can be used as a framework for developing and implementing an environmental education program for preschool children.

— *Begin with simple experiences.* Young children learn best through experiences that relate to what is already familiar and comfortable. Thus, the best place to start is in an environment similar to what they already know. For example, focus on a single tree in a backyard or playground before venturing into a heavily wooded area.

— *Provide frequent positive experiences outdoors.* Because children learn best through direct, concrete experiences, they need to be immersed in the outdoor environment to learn about it. Optimally, the exposure should be provided on an almost daily basis. A one-time trip to a park or nature preserve will have very limited impact on young children. Provide ongoing, simple experiences with the grass, trees, and insects in environments close to home or school rather than spending time and energy arranging for day trips to unfamiliar places your child may seldom visit. In addition to investigating the elements of the natural world already present in an outdoor setting, you can use many different strategies to transform a typical playground into an environmental yard. Start by adding bird feeders, wind socks, flower and vegetable gardens, tree houses, rock piles, and logs. Then, provide your child with tools for experimenting and investigating.

— Focus on "experiencing" rather than "teaching." Because young children learn through discovery and self-initiated activities, an adult should serve more as a facilitator than a teacher. Learning among young children requires active involvement — hands-on manipulation, sensory engagement, and self-initiated explorations. Young children should not be expected to "watch and listen" for any length of time, nor should they be expected to always follow your lead or agenda. Focus on what children find of interest rather than competing for attention through adult-selected activities and materials.

— *Demonstrate a personal interest in and enjoyment of the natural world.* Your expressions of interest in and enjoyment of the natural world are critical to your child's interest in the environment. Your own sense of wonder, more than your scientific knowledge, will ignite and sustain a child's love of nature. Therefore, even parents with a minimal background in science should not be intimidated by the thought of implementing an environmental education program for young children. Feelings are more important than facts when introducing young children to the world of nature.

— *Model caring and respect for the natural environment. Parents should model caring and respect for the world of nature.* Talking to children about taking care of the Earth is far less effective than demonstrating simple ways of expressing care. Care and respect can be modeled by gently handling plants and animals in the classroom, establishing or maintaining outdoor habitats for wildlife, properly disposing of trash, and recycling or reusing as many materials as possible.

— *Young children often develop an emotional attachment to what is familiar and comfortable to them.* If they are to develop a sense of connectedness with the natural world, they need frequent positive experiences with the outdoors. Providing opportunities for such experiences and sharing them with young children is the essence of environmental education. Environmental education for the early years focuses primarily on young children exploring and enjoying the world of nature under the guidance and with the companionship of caring adults.

DEVELOPING ENVIRONMENTAL PROGRAMMES FOR SCHOOL CHILDREN

It is neceesary that all schools should develop an environmental conservation and management programme to develop students's knowledge and skills in theoretical and applied environmental conservation management. The course should build on a fundamental understanding of ecological and biogeographical principles, demonstrating the way ecology is applied to the management of environmental problems, for example biological pest control and restoration.

Understanding the role of long-term ecological dynamics, especially human/environment interactions is an important part of the present and future management for conservation. The development of environmental and biodiversity protection, and the conservation movement, has played an increasing role in mainstream government. The relative success of policy for conservation, in particular those based on ecological principles, has been the subject of much debate and analysis, and forms an interesting and important area for critical assessment. The way in which theoretical principles are translated into practice can be problematic for a variety of reasons. Experiencing problems first hand is an important way of training students for situations likely to be encountered in the workplace.

The programmme shoul aim to

— develop a detailed knowledge of the theory and principles of applied ecology;

— ensure a thorough understanding of the historical and pre-historical influences of humans on the environment, and the implications of these interrelations to present and future conservation management;

— consider the role of biogeographical principles in conservation management, including such aspects as nature reserve design, endemic species and the implications of introductions of exotic species to island biota;

— study the way in which the conservation/environmental movement has developed and the influence this has had on policy making and implementation of policies for environmental protection;

— develop an appreciation of species and habitat management techniques, in particular studying the difficulties of putting theory into practice and the importance of monitoring the effects of management.

Learning Outcomes

On completion of the course students should have achieved the following learning outcomes:

— have a detailed knowledge and understanding of the principles and practice of applied ecology and biogeography;

— be able to demonstrate a fundamental knowledge of prehistorical and historical human/environment relationships and show how these influence present and future environmental and conservation management;

— be aware of the main national and international environmental and conservation protection policies and the way in which these are implemented;

— be able to critically examine the application of ecological and biogeographical theory to environmental and conservation management, for example island biogeography theory, metapopulations and population modelling;

— have a detailed understanding of species and habitat management techniques and appreciate the practical issues concerned with implementing habitat management plans.

The course should begin by covering theoretical and applied aspects of ecology and biogeography, with particular emphasis on population, community, landscape and ecosystem ecology. Biogeographical principles should be covered in depth as a detailed understanding of the distribution and biodiversity of species is fundamental to species conservation management The relevance and application of these principles to environmental and conservation management should be stressed throughout.

An understanding of pre-historical and historical human/ environmental relationships is important in appreciating how and why landscapes have developed. Emphasis should be placed on historical (post-Domesday) change, considering the role of traditional management techniques, species and habitat change and landscape processes.

A study of the value judgements in conservation and the environment movement should form the basis of examining the development of legislation for conservation and environmental protection and the role of governments and non-governmental bodies. The various designations for protecting areas for nature conservation, financial incentives for schemes such as environmentally sensitive areas and countryside stewardship should be considered in detail through case studies and discussion groups. Evaluation for nature conservation should be studied.

Global conservation and environmental management should be considered on a case study basis. In particular the impact of forestry and agriculture on species and habitats should form the basis of studying conservation measures.

Habitat types, habitat conservation and management should be studied through a combination of theory and practice. The structure and design of management plans and their implementation should form a focus for particular aspects of habitat management.

ENVIRONMENTAL LITERACY—AWARENESS OF ENVIRONMENTAL ISSUES

The term "environmental literacy" has been used for several years in relation to environmental education without much disciplined reference to debates about literacy. It has been used hitherto in the environmental education literature, but while it has been given working definitions, these have not been derived directly from a systematic engagement with literacy debates within language and literature studies. As part of the American work on "standards", Roth provides a framework for environmental literacy with relation to knowledge, affect, skills and behaviour at three levels of competence (nominal, functional and operational). For UNESCO, Marcinkowski provides a set of nine statements which amount to what environmental literacy might be taken to be, relating to knowledge, understanding, attitudes and active involvement. In Scotland, curriculum planners have included environmental literacy as one of the four goals of "environmental citizenship", defining it in terms of "knowledge and understanding of the components of the system" While each of these definitions of environmental literacy might have its practical uses, none is overtly grounded in the primary academic debate about the nature of literacy.

Functional, cultural and critical literacies

Many kinds of literacy have been identified. In relation to language development, however, whence the term derives, it is common to distinguish between functional, cultural, critical, and sometimes academic literacies. The last-mentioned refers specifically to the ability to deal with written texts in the registers common to academic writing; thus academic literacy is deemed necessary for academic advancement.

Functional literacy

Functional literacy is the ability to decode what is encoded within the black marks on the white paper into intelligible words, phrases and clauses, and to understand their literal meaning on a superficial level. Functional literacy, for example, allows you to read a sign bearing an instruction, such as "Stop!" and to act upon it. It allows you to read a story but does not account for whether you can draw any implications from it. Functional literacy (with relation to print) can therefore be taught through the learning of phonic rules. It is not directly concerned with reading for meaning. However, it does involve the ability to recognise the surface meaning of words and phrases in context: for instance, to understand "stop" in constructions such as "pull out the organ stop", "forgot to use a full stop" and "Danger - Stop!". Statistics concerning rates of literacy and illiteracy generally relate to functional literacy, and obscure the fact that what it takes to be functionally literate varies considerably from time to time and place to place.

Cultural literacy

The work of E.D. Hirsch has an enormous effect on literacy teaching in the United States and a considerable effect elsewhere, not least because of the author's closeness to the Reagan administration. Hirsch actually produced a list of "what every American needs to know", on the assumption that social and cultural cohesion depends on the ability to understand the significance American society places on, for example, Thanksgiving; not merely its existence as, say, a public holiday. Like functional literacy, cultural literacy is, in a sense, passive: it is the ability to know the received wisdom about some cultural event or institution rather than to make meaning for yourself. However, it is a powerful idea, the ramifications of which can be seen in the various ways in which governments around the world have begun, or continued, to use national curricula to reinforce national identities

Critical literacy

Critical literacy implies the ability to make sense in your own terms of the ideational potential of a text. It includes the ability to "get behind" the text to interpret it in terms of its ideological underpinnings: to distinguish, for example, between factual account, polemic and propaganda. "Critical" here is used in a double sense. On the one hand it has a long pedigree in the liberal-humanist tradition of literary criticism in which the "critical appreciation" of texts demanded an extended personal response and evaluation of the text as work of art: an exploration of the reader's initial affective response. On the other hand, it can refer to Habermas's conception of "critical-emancipatory" knowledge whereby the reader responds to the text not merely as a naive individual who can only "interpret", albeit for practical ends, but as one who understands the cultural, social and political forces that shape the text, and can therefore guard against being taken in by it. Because of this dual use of the term "critical" (the personally engaged as opposed to the socially critical), late twentieth century readings of texts have varied from the overtly personal to the apparently dispassionate and deliberately political: Marxist readings, feminist readings, ecofeminist readings and so on.

Functional environmental literacy

Functional print literacy can be measured by objective tests, which can be purely summative, or may be diagnostic if subjected to miscue analysis, which analyses reader's errors. Functional literacy is not just a matter of knowing what words mean, but of being able to find out what they mean in the context of whole sentences by the use of phonic and contextual cues. Functional literacy also involves being able to read words referring to commonplace abstractions (beauty, goodness, fear etc.). It involves literal comprehension.

Functional environmental literacy must, therefore, refer not only to the ability to remember what an oak tree is, but to recognise one; not only to recognise several trees within a given area, but to know whether they form part of a wood or an area of parkland. Functional environmental literacy must also involve the ability to ascertain, from contextual cues, what something half known is likely to be: for instance, to make an informed guess, using observation, at the types of woodland flower within a beech copse overlying chalk rather than an oak wood on more acid soil.

Functional literacy is not, therefore, a mere prerequisite to more advanced forms of literacy, but involves a series of complex skills and an accumulation of knowledge which has unlimited capacity for growth. Arguably, much science education in schools focuses chiefly on what is defined here as functional literacy, whether or not this entirely reflects intentions. Certainly, its role in environmental education should not be underestimated.

Both cultural and critical literacy are impossible without functional literacy. Just as the ability to decode print is a prerequisite to the development of deeper levels of comprehension of the passage to be read, so is knowledge of the natural world a condition of the development of awareness of environmental issues and of the ability to take effective action.

However, functional environmental literacy is not enough because it does not, of itself, engage the learner (though many learners may already be highly motivated), and it does not engage either with the crucial notion of what the environment means, either to others or to the learner. Environmental education, therefore, must never abandon its scientific knowledge base, but must always move beyond it, so that scientific knowledge is used to inform what are essentially human value judgments. In terms of environmental literacy, we must acknowledge the importance of the functional but place it alongside the cultural, and see both as conditions of the critical, as only critical environmental literacy can facilitate effective environmental action.

Cultural environmental literacy

Cultural literacy refers to the ability to understand the significance that society attaches to cultural icons. Such icons include, of course, living natural objects: national parks; the Californian redwood; the English oak. An increased cultural environmental literacy would be gained by a reading of Schama's Landscape and Memory, in which the author discusses a series of landscapes of rich significance to contemporary societies in terms of cultural history with respect to the ways in which these landscapes have been viewed, used and reshaped over a millennium. One of the abiding impressions gained from a reading of Landscape and Memory is that the landscapes in question have often been strongly shaped by cultural and social forces throughout the period in question. Schama effectively dispels the still partly-held misconception, for example, that much of England was covered with virgin forest until the last couple of hundred years.

On one level, a degree of cultural environmental literacy merely enables one to recognise the significance of natural images in human culture, along with some recognition of why and to whom they are significant: the American bald eagle, or the white dove of peace, for example. However, it also allows for an understanding of why the landscape itself is as it is, shaped not merely by climate, glaciation and topography, but by arguments about enclosure, the need for timber and patterns of land ownership dating back many centuries. While functional environmental literacy develops knowledge of what natural things are, cultural environmental literacy enables us to explain why they are there when the causes are clearly not simply geological or climatic with no apparent human intervention.

Cultural literacy depends on a degree of acceptance of cultural hegemony: it links the learner with a dominant value system. The culturally literate individual in England will know what is implied by the term "heart of oak", or understand the English Lake District as a kind of symbol of Wordsworthian Romanticism, even though these conceptions may be more associated with English "high culture" than with popular culture, as well as having no scientific basis. Cultural literacy refers more to cultural heritage than to cultural analysis. The subtitle of Hirsch's book is "What every American needs to know". Insofar as cultural literacy is empowering, it empowers by giving the learner access to socially powerful perspectives; cultural literacy alone does not enable the learner to act upon that knowledge, once acquired. Effective action requires critical literacy.

Critical environmental literacy

Critical literacy is the ability to understand the text on a deeper and more creative level: the ability to discuss the use of genre in context, to question the motives and ideology of the text, and to explore and develop personal (and broader social) response to it. Critical environmental literacy must then imply the power to develop an understanding of the factors that contribute to environmental change and to have a view on how to further to oppose that change in a way which can be translated into action. Critical environmental literacy involves the ability to explore questions such as "What does [a place or an issue] mean to me?"; "What does it mean to us, or to others?"; "What are the consequences of carrying on in this way [in relation to this place or this issue]?"; "Should we act differently, and if so how?"; "How do we translate our values into effective action - and are our values themselves ready for change as a result of what we now know or feel?"

Critical literacy cannot be effectively developed without good levels of both functional and cultural literacy, though the latter are arguably pointless without the former. Critical environmental literacy relies on functional environmental literacy because both environmental debate and environmental action rely on information. Critical environmental literacy relies on cultural literacy not simply because environmental debate and action need to be grounded in an awareness of the norms and values of, say, national cultures, but because influence on environmental change demands an understanding of the norms and values of the dominant culture.

ROLE OF MASS MEDIA IN ENVIRONMENTAL AWARENESS

Like most other developing countries, India is today facing environmental problems of enormous magnitude that adversely affect the lives of its people form all walks of life. Many of these problems have resulted due to a lack of understanding and concern about environmental and sustainable development issues. This has led, among other things, to over-exploitation of natural resources and badly planned development and industrial projects. These have intensified socio-economic problems as well as created large scale air, water and soil pollution.

There are huge disparities in incomes and lifestyles of people in India. This means that a large percentage of the population lives in poverty, with few options to choose environmentally appropriate lifestyles. Others are in a position to make environmentally sensitive decisions but rarely do so, partly because of lack of awareness.

In order to ensure people make positive choices about the environmental impacts of their lifestyles, there is an urgent need to create mass scale awareness on environmental and development issues. If India's environmental problems are to be effectively tackled, then it is critical to have an informed public that understands and supports environmental initiatives.

One of the most effective ways of getting the message across to the largest possible audience in a country as vast and diverse as India is through the mass media, including television and the English and vernacular press. Both these media have the potential of being extremely effective tools for environmental communication, but have not been sufficiently exploited for this purpose so far.

The television revolution that has recently hit India provides an excellent opportunity to reach out to the literate as well as the illiterate population of the country. Since the advent of satellite television, TV today attracts audiences ranging from the educated elite to poor villagers in all parts of the county. Recognising the rapidly deteriorating environmental scenario, the Supreme Court of India in several directives has emphasised the need to use the mass media, especially TV, for promoting environmental awareness. Responding to this, the Government is now increasingly interested in allocating prime time TV slots to environmental programmes.

However, the Government has not yet been able to implement this satisfactorily. The vastly increased penetration of TV to all sections of Indian society remains under-utilised in terms of this objective. There is a great dearth of good programmes on TV, and very few incisive articles on environmental issues in the written press. Most environmental documentaries shown on TV today attract few viewers because of the academic or pedantic manner in which they are presented. Similarly, although many English newspapers are now carrying more and more features on environmental issues, they are usually superficially researched and poorly written. Vernacular papers still carry very little or no environmental news.

ROLE OF ZOOS AND AQUARIUMS IN ENVIRONMENTAL AWARENESS

A conservation education not to tell the community what can or can not be done, but rather to give them the information to look at the environment in different ways. The community is not only the visitors but everybody who can be reached by zoos or aquariums. Facing varous environmental problems, what can zoos and aquariums do? First they must look for the cause of the problems: lack of community awareness on the environment. They must develop a community awareness and community involvement to counteract the lack of knowledge and information about the environment by giving conservation education.

For example the SeaWorld Indonesia has taken such a commitment. To support the its Education unit provides accurate information for the exhibits for the regular visitors and school groups by using graphic panels, direct conversation and feeding show presentations. The graphics should specially designed for educational and entertaining purposes. Not only do they contain ordinary information such as the animal's name, distribution and diet but also interesting facts about the animals, their role in the ecosystem and what the community can do to save the animal and its environment. By giving the written information in a systematic and interesting way, they will be easily understood and promote empathy among the visitors.

However some visitors will only look at the exhibits and read only the animal's name, which means they miss the conservation messages. To solve this problem, SeaWorld Indonesia provides Education staffs to explain the invaluable information. Having direct conversation with visitors means a two-way communication which is much more effective for deeper understanding, for example how to get involved in saving the environment. Education staffs also give a feeding show presentation. During the presentation, they share conservation messages and emphasize the importance of the wise use of environmental resources for the future.

Above all, the most important way to create environmental awareness is by touching, holding and feeding the animals. This provides a special experience and generates deep impression which will be remembered by the visitors. For this purpose, SeaWorld Indonesia provides a large Touch Pool, inhabited by harmless animals. Education guides accompany the visitors in touching, feeding of the animals and to share their knowledge.

SeaWorld Indonesia has developed a school program called Sekolah Bersama Ikan (School With The Fish). They made worksheets for all class levels from kindergarten to senior high school. The programs are informative, interactive and exciting. All students are given the worksheet. With worksheet in hand, the student can explore the wonders of the aquariums. The worksheet differs from what students find in their schools by asking leading questions which require the student to closely observe the animal or display and interpret their findings. Attractive illustrations stimulate their imaginations.

The education staffs are available to guide and assist the students. Over 600.000 students have participated in this program. On the one hand, the program has succeeded but on the other hand the large number of students have made the program less effective. To keep this school program running effectively, every ten students should be accompanied by one teacher. All students have to answer the questions on the worksheet and return it to the teacher for scoring. The education program can also be done outdoors so they can see and learn in the real environment. This method will stimulate their sense of adventure and discovery.

SeaWorld Indonesia develops outreach programs for the community that has a direct impact on the environment, such as the fishing villages. They visit schools in the fishing villages once a month. The teach the children through interesting games and quizzes about marine life, how precious the sea is with its large variety of sea creatures and the importance of protecting their future by the wise use of marine recourses. They were very excited and asked many questions during this program. At the end of this program, they gave them presents. Since 1995, this program has been conducted in North Jakarta, Kepulauan Seribu (Thousand Islands), Karimunjawa in Central Java trough to Lampung.

Beginning this year SeaWorld Indonesia has also developed an outreach program for private schools especially Play Groups and Kindergartens. They introduced sea animals which can be touched likes sea stars, sea cucumbers and turtles before they visit SeaWorld. This program helps the children to learn and to appreciate the sea and the marine life so that in future, they will also become involved in the conservation efforts to save the valuable heritage.

To encourage more people to participate in marine conservation efforts, SeaWorld has organised special events such as "Reuse and Recycle Competition" and "Drawing Competition on Save the Marine Life". SeaWorld Indonesia has participated in some national and international events which were related to marine conservation, e.g. Reef Check '97 which was held in the framework of International Year of The Reef 1997.

Modern Zoos and Aquariums have a very important role in conservation education. Many methods and programs have to be developed in order to reach all social classes. One of the most important ways is to use interactive methods which can give a long-lasting memorable experience. More and more people will become involve in conservation efforts when they have empathy with nature.

7

Environmental Education Programmes for Attitude Changes among Children

Environmental literacy depends on a personal commitment and motivation to help ensure environmental quality and quality of life. This commitment and motivation often begins with an awareness of one's immediate surroundings. Environmental educators can help foster learners' innate curiosity and enthusiasm, providing them with continuing opportunities to explore their environment and engaging them in direct discovery of the world around them.

As learners develop and apply analysis and action skills, as they have the opportunity to make their own decisions and think more critically about their choices and as they hear stories of success, they are learning that what they do individually and in groups can make a difference. This locus of control, or sense that they have the ability to influence the outcome of a situation, is important in helping learners develop a sense of empowerment and a sense of personal responsibility - further key aspects of environmental education.

In order to reach this goal of environmental literacy, environmental education programmes must be effective. Effective environmental education programmes are relevant to the mission of the agency or organization, to the educational objectives of the audience, and to the everyday lives of the individual learners. They involve stakeholders in all stages of the programme, from the development of the programme to its evaluation. Effective programmes empower learners with skills to help prevent and address environmental issues and with a sense of personal and civic responsibility. Further, they are accurate and balanced, incorporating multiple perspectives and interdisciplinary aspects.

Effective environmental education programmes are instructionally sound, using "best practices" in education. And finally, effective programmes are evaluated with appropriate tools. Amidst numerous, growing and complex environmental problems, the need for the preparation of world problem solvers is as great as ever. Educators have globally accepted this role of preparing students to become critical thinkers, informed decision-makers and able communicators. In virtually every country "there is a frantic haste to develop programmes in environmental education".

The roots of this environmental education movement extend back to the nature study movement, with leaders such as John Muir and Enos Mills and their study of the natural history of plants and animals. In 1891, Wilbur Jackman wrote Nature Study for the Common Schools, which aimed to educate urban dwellers who had lost touch with the natural world. In 1896, a junior naturalist programme associated with Cornell University taught students about the natural world in the context of understanding rural agriculture.

The nature study movement contributed some of the early ideals for education that are still im-portant today in elementary science education - inquiry and discovery with first-hand observation. The conservation education movement began in response to the soil erosion, dust storms and flooding disasters of the 1930s. Initiated by resource management agencies, the goal of conservation education was to awaken Americans to the importance of conserving various natural resources.

Forester Aldo Leopold gained national fame during this era and significantly influenced the movement through his passionate essays and provocative theories. Legislation was passed giving schools land designated for nature purposes. In addition, camps sponsored by churches and agencies, such as the YMCA, used recreation to help promote an understanding of the natural world. At the same time, the progressive education movement surfaced. Led by John Dewey, the focus of progressive education was "learning by doing," incorporating learning about the environment while in the environment.

The 1950s gave rise to outdoor education, with its sole specification of the place for learning - outside the school building. Outdoor education was described by L.B. Sharp, who wrote,

> "That which can best be learned inside the classroom should be learned there; and that which can best be learned through direct experience outside the classroom, in contact with native materials and life situations, should there be learned".

This movement was in response to concerns that urban youth were not experiencing direct contact with the natural environment. Teachers were encouraged to teach many different subjects in the outdoors, giving students this opportunity. Through the nuclear testing of the 1950s and Rachel Carson's book, Silent Spring, people began to notice the impact on the environment by "unseen forces," such as nuclear fallout and modern agricultural practices.

During the 1960s and into the early 1970s, the environmental movement contributed a human aspect to the evolution of environmental education, helping people realize the impact humans have on the natural and built environment. The 1970 Earth Day celebrations were "a landmark expression of public support for a realignment of values and a new respect for the environment". This set the stage for the transition of education about the environment and in the environment to education for the environment.

In 1972, the United Nations Conference on the Human Environment, held in Stockholm, Sweden, recommended the establishment of environmental education programmes on an international level. Following this recommendation, the United Nations Educational, Scientific, and Cultural Organization (UNESCO) sponsored a series of international environmental education workshops and conferences. United Nations representatives met in the former Yugoslavia in 1975 to define environmental education and establish its basic objectives.

The Belgrade Charter was adopted at this conference, providing a widely accepted goal statement for environmental education. It states:

> "The goal of environmental education is to develop a world population that is aware of, and concerned about, the total environment and its associated problems, and which has the knowledge, attitudes, skills, motivation, and commitment to work individually and collectively toward solutions of current problems and the prevention of new ones".

In 1977, representatives from 66 member nations and observers from two nonmember nations gathered for the world's first intergovernmental conference on environmental education. This conference, held in Tbilisi in the former Soviet Republic of Georgia, led to the release of an official statement on environmental education the Tbilisi Declaration. Built on the Belgrade Charter, the Tbilisi Declaration acclaimed "the important role of environmental education in the preservation and improvement of the world's environment, as well as in the sound and balanced development of the world's communities".

In addition to establishing overall goals of environmental education, the Tbilisi Declaration established the following objectives of environmental education:

— *Awareness*—to acquire an awareness and sensitivity to the total environment and its allied problems;

— *Knowledge*—to gain a variety of experiences in and acquire a basic understanding of, the environment and its associated problems;

— *Attitudes*—to acquire a set of values and feelings of concern for the environment and motivation for actively participating in environmental improvement and protection;

— *Skills*—to acquire the skills for identifying and solving environmental problems; and

— *Participation*—to encourage citizens to be actively involved at all levels in working toward resolution of environmental problems.

The Tbilisi Declaration constitutes the framework, principles and guidelines for environmental education at all geographical levels - local through international and for all age groups, both inside and outside the formal school system. The Belgrade Charter and the Tbilisi Declaration are con-sidered founding documents of the field and provide the foundation for much of what has been done in the field since 1978. More recently, the 1987 Brundtland Commission and the 1992 United Nations Conference on Environment and Development have influenced environmental education at an international level.

The passing of the National Environmental Education Act of 1970 in the United States reflected a national commitment to environmental education. This act stated that environmental education "is intended to promote among citizens the awareness and understanding of the environment, our relationship to it, and the concern and responsible action necessary to assure our survival and to improve the quality of life". The 1990 National Environmental Education Act reaffirms the purpose of the earlier act. It also focuses on schools as the place for effective environmental education, while recognizing the importance of non-formal avenues for educating citizens, communities and the workforce. In summary, environmental education is not the presentation of information. Environmental education helps learners achieve environmental literacy, which has attitude and behavior components in addition to a knowledge component. Thus, the goal of environmental education is to instill in learners knowledge about the environment, positive attitudes toward the environment, competency in citizen action skills, and a sense of empowerment.

Further, while the audience is often youth, environmental education is intended for all - youth and adults, as well as individuals and organized groups.

ELEMENTS OF EFFECTIVE ENVIRONMENTAL EDUCATION PROGRAMMES

— Effective environmental education programmes are relevant to the mission of the agency or organization, to the educational objectives of the audience, and to the everyday lives of the individual learners.

Good environmental education programmes are relevant relevant to the agency or organization, relevant to the audience and meaningful to their everyday lives. An agency or organization's mission and environmental priorities provide direction for programme development in environmental education, guiding the development of goals and objects and their choice of target audience. Tying environmental education programmes to the agency or organization's primary purpose helps focus programme development and justify funding, prevent the establishment of generic environmental education programmes, and aid in programme efficiency and sustainability.

However, it is not enough for an agency or organization to consider only its mission or purpose. Environmental education programmes are often distinguished from informative or interpretive programmes, as they have objectives beyond information dispersal and involve working with an audience that often has pre-defined learning objectives. A school group, for example, has pre-defined learning objectives in the form of a curriculum what teachers will teach, the order in which concepts should be covered, and expected knowledge and skills. A scout group would also have learning objectives, which might take the form of earning badges or patches. The key to relevant environmental education programmes is finding commonalities among the existing learning objectives and the agencies or organization's mission and priorities. By doing so, the needs of both the provider and the audience are met. Teachers or leaders of the groups that will be participating in the programme can often help find these commonalities by providing and explaining materials that offer learning objectives.

Effective environmental education programmes and materials need to present information and ideas in a way that is relevant to the learners. For example, a programme on endangered species would be more relevant to students in Florida if the manatee were used as an example, rather than the Siberian tiger.

This need for relevance stems from children's cognitive development, as they develop the ability to think concretely before they can think abstractly. When programmes move beyond what is relevant and meaningful, learners don't have the chance to build their learning on what they already know - learning becomes too abstract.

Thus, content is more effectively conveyed when embedded in a local context, giving learners a chance to explore and experience what's around them. The sensitivity, knowledge and skills needed for this local connection provide a base for moving out into larger systems, broader issues and an expanding understanding of causes, connections and consequences. Likewise, skill building and application must be couched within the context of solving real problems problems that directly affect learners either at home, at school or in their community. When environmental education is taught in the place where they live and through authentic situations, a learner's own experiences become a part of their education.

Enjoyable learning experiences also help make programmes more relevant to the learners. Many environmental educators realize the value of learners having direct contact with nature. Daniel Kriesberg, in A Sense of Place, writes, "They need to be outside. They need to explore, get dirty, find stuff - they need to have fun".

The problem, explains Kriesberg, is that many learners don't have these opportunities. Small bits of wild places where kids can explore are disappearing and time to visit them becomes more and more rare, resulting in the "extinction of experience." Thus, environmental educators need to reintroduce learners to their local area by exploring and experiencing it, by learning about it and celebrating it. By doing so, environmental educators help learners develop a sense of wonder and a sense of place, fostering the awareness and appreciation that motivate them to further questioning, better understanding, and appropriate concern and action.

— Effective environmental education programmes involve stakeholders in all stages of the programme, from the development of the programme to its evaluation.

Successful programmes bring a coalition of stakeholders together to design, implement and evaluate a programme that meets their needs. Stakeholders are those that have a stake in the programme that is developed. They are they people who care about a programme, are willing to develop a commitment to it and are best able to offer input into it. These stakeholders might be teachers, funders, agency supervisors, community leaders, landowners, extension workers, parents, and curriculum developers.

While it would be impractical to consult a large number of stakeholders on every decision, their input and participation is essential in the beginning stages. Their participation lends a variety of perspectives to the programme, shaping the programme focus and audience. Their participation also helps achieve buy-in early in the process, so that as the programme is developed, it is more likely to be used.

Another advantage of using stakeholders is that it reinforces the image of community partnership and/or ownership and interest in the programme. Stakeholders are also important during the evaluation phases of the programme, as they can offer input about what information to gather, how to gather it and ultimately how to share it with important audiences. While this stakeholder approach can seem cumbersome, most organizations using a stakeholder approach believe the strengths outweigh the extra time and effort needed to manage the process.

Organizations using this approach have found several things helpful. In developing a team of stakeholders, think about who will be the ultimate users of the results and try to structure your team so that the results are channeled directly to those end-user groups. After identifying which groups should be represented on your team of stakeholders, select who, specifically, should represent each group on the team. Select team members who are enthusiastic, willing to represent his or her group, willing to commit to the project and those who have opinions but not "axes to grind." Strive for diversity among team members, not limiting members to those holding formal leadership positions within their groups or those that are the "most involved" or "best".

Once a stakeholder team is established, communication is key. Responsibilities need to be clarified early and often through multiple modes of communication. Make sure your team knows they are acting in an advisory capacity and not in a decision-making capacity. Work with the team to identify rules and roles for smooth and effective operation. Group facilitation skills can also aid in effective stakeholder team operation.

— Effective environmental education programmes empower learners with skills to help prevent and address environmental issues and with a sense of personal and civic responsibility.

Awareness and knowledge of environmental processes and systems play an important role in environmental education. But awareness and knowledge alone do not make a programme an environmental education programme. And when considering the goal of environmental education, research shows that knowledge and attitudes are not the only variables at play. While knowledge and attitudes alone don't help or harm the environment, human behaviors do. Behaviors, of course, are supported by knowledge and attitudes, but there is not a direct cause-and effect- progression from knowledge to attitude to behavior, as educators have long believed. How can educators help learners behave in environmentally responsible ways?

Some have turned to environmental communication techniques and social marketing theories to successfully address behavior change. School-based environmental education, however, differs from environmental communications and social marketing in that it doesn't always directly target specific behaviors, particularly in the context of controversial issues. Instead, environmental education attempts to teach students "how to think" and not "what to think." Rather than directing learners in a specific course of behavior, environmental education helps learners form the capacity to collect and analyze information, make informed decisions, and participate fully in civic life.

This requires more than the awareness and knowledge of environmental processes and systems and positive attitudes toward the environment; it requires procedural knowledge of how to affect change and the competency in citizen action skills needed to participate fully in civic life. Educators can help develop this procedural knowledge and competency in citizen action skills by providing opportunities to define an issue, determine if action is warranted, identify others involved in the issues, select appropriate action strategies, create and evaluate an action plan, implement the plan and evaluate the results. Educators can also provide opportunities to build skills in oral and written communication, conflict resolution, and leadership and opportunities to participate in the political or regulatory process, consumer action, and community service.

Thus, environmental education involves a learning progression from awareness to action, a progression mirrored in the objectives set forth by the Tbilisi Declaration described above. Environmental literacy depends on a personal commitment and motivation to help ensure environmental quality and quality of life. This commitment and motivation often begins with an awareness of one's immediate surroundings. Environmental educators can help foster learners' innate curiosity and enthusiasm, providing them with continuing opportunities to explore their environment and engaging them in direct discovery of the world around them.

Furthermore, this learning progression is not necessarily linear nor is it hierarchical. As learners develop and apply analysis and action skills, as they have the opportunity to make their own decisions and think more critically about their choices and as they hear stories of success, they are learning that what they do individually and in groups can make a difference. This locus of control, or sense that they have the ability to influence the outcome of a situation, is important in helping learners develop a sense of empowerment and a sense of personal responsibility - further key aspects of environmental education.

— Effective environmental education programmes are accurate and balanced, incorporating multiple perspectives and interdisciplinary aspects.

Environmental education has been criticized by a number of groups and individuals for lacking credibility and accuracy. Environmental education has been criticized by a number of groups and individuals for lacking credibility and accuracy. A book by Michael Sanera and Jane Shaw, Facts Not Fear: A Parent's Guide to Teaching Children About the Environment, has played a central role in this challenge. Children, according to this book, are being scared by misinformation presented by their teachers and textbooks. Katherine Kersten, chair of the

Center of the American Experiment in Minneapolis, Minnesota, echoes this concern describing environmental education as resulting in a "we're all going to die" sense of hopelessness.

In April 1997, the Independent Commission on Environmental Education released their assessment on environmental education materials, "Are We Building Environmental Literacy?" Sponsored by the George C. Marshall Institute, the Commission reviewed approximately 70 different resources for science and environmental education, including science textbooks and curricula produced by non-profit agencies, government agencies, and private individuals. This assessment, too, challenges the credibility of some environmental education materials, primarily with regard to the treatment of controversial issues.

In response to this wave of criticism, the National Environmental Education and Training Foundation (NEETF) prepared a briefing report. The report states, "Children and adults receive messages about the environment from many places - television, movies, books, newspapers, and magazines. The message may be about the environment, but Environmental Education, as practiced by concerned professionals, is very different from casual information or advocacy to promote a particular point of view". The report outlines the "facts" concerning environmental education. Environmental educators, according to the report, are advocates for balanced and scientifically accurate education. Guidelines estab-lished by the North American Association for Environmental Education help ensure this balance and accuracy. The report cites characteristics for environmental education that are recommended by the NAAEE's Environmental Education Materials: Guidelines for Excellence:

— factual accuracy - materials should reflect sound theories and well-documented facts;

— balanced presentation of differing viewpoints and theories - differences of opinion and competing scientific explanations should be presented in a balanced way; and

— openness to inquiry - materials should encourage students to explore different perspectives and form their own opinions.

Their report further states that environmental education promotes quality education and effective teaching across the disciplines. Environmental education, according to the briefing report, can help schools accomplish the eight national education goals of the Educate America Act of 1994. The National Environmental Education and Training Foundation cites a report by the State Education and Environment Roundtable, in San Diego, California, which evaluated environmental education programmes in 41 schools across 12 states. This report found environmental education programmes increasing students' knowledge of the natural sciences, language arts, mathematics, and social sciences. In addition, over seventy-five percent of the schools evaluated reported increases in grade averages and standardized test scores.

Pam Landers, project manager for the Environmental Education Teacher Preparation Project in Minnesota, has responded to the criticism surrounding environmental education in a similar manner, distinguishing environmental education from casual information and pure advocacy. Education, according to Landers, "should enable people to act intelligently, with some measure of independent thinking. People are not able to think and act intelligently "if they have been merely conditioned or coerced". Environmental education helps facilitate a student's ability "to make decisions, solve problems and conduct inquiries, using reading, communications, science, math and other skills as tools".

This recent opposition has prompted environmental educators to take a closer look at the validity, relevancy and accuracy of the field's materials and methods. The reports, books and newspaper articles challenging the credibility of environmental education are helping insure that the delivery of environmental education continues to be high quality education.

While there generally is consensus in the field for this balanced approach prescribed by NAAEE, some environmental educators believe taking more of an advocacy approach is warranted when educating for the environment. In some situations, it may be appropriate to take a less balanced, but still scientifically accurate approach. For example, it is appropriate for teachers to enforce socially accepted behaviors, such as no kicking or no cheating in class. By the same token, it may be justifiable for agencies to provide an unbalanced approach to socially accepted behaviors in areas such as boating safety, endangered species protection, and aquatic habitat improvement. But when educational messages drift to uncertain waters, such as pollution sources, private property rights or other controversial areas, agencies may be wise to avoid an advocacy message and instead revert to presenting multiple views and perspectives.

Another example of when it may be appropriate to take a less balanced approach is when urgent and specific behavior change is needed or when the target audience is adults who have chosen to participate in the programme. However, these situations perhaps may be viewed more accurately as using environmental communications or social marketing, rather than "true" environmental education.

— Effective environmental education programmes are instructionally sound, using "best practices" in education.

According to the Wisconsin Department of Instruction, educational programmes and curricula should be developed in response to theories of learning, such as Piaget's theory of cognitive development, constructivism, multiple intelligences, and learning styles. In order for environmental education programmes to be effective in an educational sense, they must also be congruent with the way people learn. The following are descriptions of theories of learning and their implications, which can guide curriculum planning, programme development and methodology in environmental education.

IMPLICATIONS OF THEORIES OF LEARNING IN ENVIRONMENTAL EDUCATION

Piaget's Cognitive development theory

Until about the 1930s, children were considered to be miniature adults intellectually; children differed from adults only in the quantity of knowledge they had acquired. Through research by Piaget and others, it became clear that children think and learn in ways that are different from adults. As children develop, they reorganize and re-construct their base of knowledge, replacing one set of assumptions with another.

Piaget identified four cognitive stages through which an individual may progress from birth through adolescence: sensorimotor, preoperational, concrete operation and formal operational. This sequence is invariantly ordered, and some refer to these stages, respectively, as the active child, the intuitive student, the practical student, and the reflective student. Development is associated with the passage from one stage of operation to another and is a function of experience and maturation.

Piaget's theory implies that instructional methods and content need to be consistent with how students develop cognitively, as children cannot "learn" if they cannot understand what they are being asked to learn. Real knowledge, according to Piaget, can only occur when the task is useful to the student and when the student is psychologically ready.

Teaching, then, is the act of creating environments that allow for students' cognitive structures to change and emerge - environments that provide for learning opportunities at a level just above a student's current cognitive level. Many programmes provide learners with choices, as learner tend to choose learning experiences appropriate for their cognitive structures. Applied to environmental education, curricula should be developed so that they facilitate stage-relevant thinking and allow students to discover for themselves the logical connections between object or events. A further implication is for students to have many opportunities to explore the natural world and think about it within their various stages of intellectual development.

Constructivism

For most of this century, behaviorism has driven educational practice. This model of learning assumes that students are a blank slate on which the knowledge of others is simply written. Research since the mid-1970s has led to a new model - constructivism. Jean Piaget was an early supporter of constructivism, believing strongly that learning occurs as a result of dynamic interactions between individuals and physical and social environments. Thus, rather than being directly transmitted from teachers and books to students, knowledge is actively constructed from students actions in the environment. According to Piaget, the development of knowledge is a process of continual construction and reorganization.

Another key tenet of constructivism is the interplay between newly constructed knowledge and the learner's prior knowledge. Ausubel et al. stated that the most important factor influencing learning is what the learner already knows.

Learning occurs by "actively constructing knowledge, weighing new information against . . . previous understanding, thinking about and working through discrepancies . . . and coming to a new understanding". Learning can occur only when the new idea or concept can be integrated into the learner's existing conceptual system. Thus, the context of learning is important, as the situation must be both somewhat familiar and somewhat new. When the learner cannot integrate the new material with previous knowledge, rote learning occurs.

For educators, constructivism implies that instructional methods need to be consistent with how students construct knowledge and that the çontext or content must be relevant. Clough and Wood-Robinson agree, arguing that classroom learning would be improved if teachers could build upon the learners' ideas rather than ignore them. Their research suggests that students "have a great deal of knowledge about a subject from out-of-school sources".

Teachers, according to this research, should draw preexisting knowledge into the classroom, using what learners already know and what is familiar to them as a basis for knowledge restructuring. Anderson describes a three-stage process that can be used when teaching for conceptual change. In the first, or preparation, phase, learners "begin to think about the phenomena that will be explained in the unit, discuss their own explanations, and become aware of the limitations of their naïve explanations". This stage is followed by a presentation phase, in which teachers explain key principles and theories. The final stage is application and integration.

In this stage, learners apply the scientific principles to new phenomena and integrate those principles and theories into their personal knowledge. These implications translate into elements useful to environmental education - programmes that are learnercentered and involve active learning. In other words, environmental education is something students do, not something that is done to them. These aspects are at the heart of experiential education, a methodology that closely parallels constructivism. A central tenet of experiential education is that learning is an active process, occurring when experiences build upon previous experiences in a positive way and incorporate interaction between the learner and the environment.

Experiential education drives several specific instructional methods, including service learning, problem- or project-based learning, and field-based instruction. These methods are proving to be quite effective in environmental education and hold promise for motivating students and improving student learning and academic performance.

Constructivism also supports cooperative learning. Cooperative learning is a teaching strategy that allows learners to work in small groups to explore a new idea, gather information, discuss ideas, apply concepts and solve a problem. Research has also shown that cooperative learning is an effective instructional approach for student achievement in reading, math, science and thinking skills. Research by Solomon, Nastasi and Clements and Lazarowitz and Karsenty has also shown that cooperative learning has positive effects on students' social skills and interactions with their peers. By incorporating cooperative learning into environmental education programmes, students have the opportunity to gain communication skills, leadership skills and the ability to work with others - all of which are important aspects of environmental literacy.

Gardner's Theory of Multiple Intelligences and McCarthy's Research on Learning Styles

Howard Gardner's theory outlines seven ways of recognizing a person's intellect. They are: visualspatial, bodily-kinesthetic, musical, logicalmathematical, verbal-linguistic, interpersonal, and intrapersonal.

According to Gardner, the main value of his theory is that it helps educators acknowledge differences in how students learn. His theory of multiple intelligences is related to research on learning styles by McCarthy, who describes four major learning styles.

One of the four learning styles is the imaginative learning style. Imaginative learners perceive information concretely and process it reflectively. Learning occurs through listening and sharing ideas, and the imaginative learner functions through social interaction. Analytic learners, the second type, perceive information abstractly and process it reflectively.

An analytic learner prefers sequential thinking, need details and value what experts have to offer. The third type, common sense learners, perceives information abstractly and processes it actively. Common sense learners are practical and enjoy hands-on learning, looking for immediate use of what is being learned. Finally, dynamic learners perceive information concretely and process it actively. Dynamic learners learn by trial and error and self-discovery, being excited by anything that is new.

McCarthy's multiple learning styles research and Gardner's theory of multiple intelligences remind educators that not all students learn and respond to learning situations in the same way. Further, intelligence is not a fixed or static reality; it can be learned, taught and developed. Their research has important implications for those who develop and implement environmental education programmes.

The content, teaching methods and assessment used in an environmental education programme should allow for the expression of multiple intelligences, allowing students multiple ways of learning and showing what they know and can do. Further, content should be presented using a variety of teaching strategies (groups, physical activity, artistic variations, etc.), providing students with the opportunities to express their learning styles and their auditory, visual, tactile and kinesthetic preferences for receiving information.

EVALUATING ENVIRONMENTAL EDUCATION PROGRAMMES

Programme evaluation was born during the period of large-scale social programmes and government intervention of the 1960s and 1970s. Programme evaluation focused on guiding funding decisions, helping determine what was worth funding and what was worth doing. As evaluations were implemented, a new role emerged: increasing overall programme effectiveness by guiding improvements to the programme. Thus, today we think about programme evaluation not only in terms of something that is done as or after a programme is implemented, but also as something that is done throughout the development and implementation of the programme.

In his book, Utilization-Focused Evaluation, Michael Patton provides a useful definition of programme evaluation. Patton describes this as the systematic collection of information about the activities, characteristics, and outcomes of programmes to make judgments about the programme, improve programme effectiveness, and/or inform decisions about future programmeming.

This type of evaluation is within contextual boundaries of time, place, values and politics. Central to his definition is meeting the information needs of specific intended users. Their information needs, that is, their intended uses, focus the evaluation. Care must be taken to incorporate the stakeholders' opinions throughout the evaluation process, as this increases the likelihood that the findings will be used.

Another key aspect is the systematic collection of information about a potentially broad range of topics. Systematic data collection is emphasized as opposed to applying social science methods; programme evaluators may use research methods to gather information but they may also use other forms of systematic information that are not research-oriented. While how to define programme evaluation is a matter for discussion and negotiation, what is not negotiable is that the evaluation be data-based.These two key aspects provide guidance for environmental education programme evaluation. The evaluation should have a purpose and audience and should involve systematic data collection. Determining the purpose for or the focus of the evaluation helps direct how the evaluation process proceeds, including what and how information is collected.

There are a number of tools or methods that can be used to collect information as the programme is being developed. Comment or feedback forms, observations, interviews, focus groups, and surveys are examples. When curriculum materials are being developed, feedback by content and pedagogical experts should be a part of the development process. Individual lessons can be pilot tested or the programme in its entirety can be field-tested, both of which are critical to developing practical and useful programmes or curriculum materials. Information from these methods is used to help improve the programme or materials. Information should also be collected after the programme is complete to help the programme manager make an overall judgment of the value of the programme - often for the benefit of some external audience or decision maker. This information helps answer questions such as whether or not it worked, were goals met and should the programme be continued.

For environmental educators, changes in knowledge, attitude, intentions, and behaviors of programme participants are of interest. While important, designing an assessment to measure these changes is difficult. The questions must be specific enough to target some difference that will be measurable, and enough students must be involved to find significant differences. Further, to measure the impact of the programme, one must be able to compare students who participated in the programme with students who did not, or compare student's knowledge at two different times - before and after the programme. The National Park Education Programmes:

Making a Difference report offers some suggestions: use both strategies of measuring impact to reduce the problems associated with each; assign "equivalent" classes in the same school to be control and experimental; inform teachers of their role in the evaluation process; carefully select teachers and schools to provide a cross-section of reality in the school situation; and accept that there will be some factors that cannot be controlled.

Research and/or Discussion Relating to Student's Acheivement

In the case of school-based environmental education programmes, these needs relate to the educational objectives of schools at the classroom, district, state and national levels.

While environmental educators realize the importance of environmental education and its relevance to the daily lives of students, they must also realize that school administrators may not believe it plays a highly relevant role in meeting students' educational needs and objectives. In the midst of school reform, standards and high stakes testing, environmental education may be the last thing on their minds. Thus, environmental educators find themselves having to justify environmental education. One way of doing this is demonstrating that environmental education can improve student learning and academic performance - the very goals that school administrators are seeking.

The Environmental Protection Agency acknowledges the need for research relating to environmental education and student learning. In a recent call for proposals, the Environmental Protection Agency is seeking to fund research projects that answer the following questions: To what extent does environmental education improve student academic performance when integrated within various core subjects (such as science, social studies, language arts, etc.)? What specific characteristics of an environmental education programme and/ or the instructional practices used have the greatest impact on student performance? What are the implications of this research for linking EE with state and national education reform efforts?

These research questions lead to questions for further discussion. Where do the goals of environmental education fit within this fairly recent emphasis on improving student learning? Or is environmental educa-tion "selling out" to meet the needs of the formal education community? Not necessarily. Environmental education has much to offer formal education, including a relevant context, engaging topics and "hands-on" opportunities for learning. When the goal of improving student learning is viewed as complementary with building environmental literacy, environmental educators can help the wider education community understand that environmental education is simply good education. This will go a long way in ensuring that, in the midst of education reform and its high-stakes standards and evaluation, environmental education doesn't get lost in the shuffle.

Research and/or Discussion Relating to Education and Behavior Change

Environmental education programmes help build skills to prevent and address environmental issues. Preventing and addressing environmental issues brings us into the arena of behavior change and raises the question of how educators can affect behavior change using educational tools alone. This relates to the long-believed notion that increased knowledge will lead to increased concern, which in turn leads to behavioral change. While knowledge, attitudes and behaviors are related, the relationship is not a simple cause-and-effect progression from knowledge to attitude to behavior, as educators have long believed. Further research has indicated that there are a number of variables acting in combination to influence behavioral intentions. Variables most closely correlated with environmentally responsible actions are perceived skill in using action strategies, level of environmental sensitivity, perceived knowledge of action strategies, and locus of control.

A recent article in the Journal of Environmental Education takes this a step further. Researchers at the Seoul National University, Korea found that the variables of locus of control and attitude are more important than knowledge and personal responsibility in terms of the effects on intention to act. Specifically, the core variable "for improving the intention to act for responsible environmental behavior is internal locus of control". The article states further, "if environmental educators want to change or to improve their subjects' intentions to act, it would be effective to use programmes and materials that can stimulate internal locus of control". The change of locus of control could be achieved by encouraging people to make their own decisions about problems and critically evaluate the opinions of others and by providing opportunities for people to apply action skills successfully.

More research, specifically longitudinal, is needed as,"research has not yet satisfactorily identified the knowledge components that are the precursors to responsible environmental behavior". This need concurs with a recommendation by Saunders, Hungerford and Volk for a national longitudinal study of changes in K-12 student behavior and behavior changes of target populations within the general public as a function of environmental education instruction and an investigation of the precursors to responsible environmental behavior within the general public. Further, research has not yet identified how transferable or generalizable skills learned through environmental education are.

While these questions relating to behavior change provide opportunities for further research, they also provide the opportunity for further discussion - the consideration of how other disciplines might contribute to the goal of environmentally responsible behavior. The emerging discipline of social marketing, for example, provides some insight into these questions. Derived from commercial marketing and behavior psychology, social marketing can be used to encourage new behaviors in groups of people.

To influence new behaviors, social marketing involves the following steps: identifying the audience and understanding what they perceive to be the barriers and benefits of their behavioral choices; designing a strategy that utilizes behavior change tools, piloting the strategy with a small segment of a community and finally, evaluating the impact of the programme once it has been implemented across a community. In contrast to environmental education's framework of building, knowledge, skills and attitudes to act on behalf of the environment, social marketing raises the possibility that people may change their behavior for motives other than environmental reasons.

Some recommendations for further research, discussion and/or training are given below:

1. *Addressing complex environmental issues through environmental education:* The literature tells us the effective environmental education programmes require content and methods that are concrete and relevant to learners. However, how do environmental educators handle the environmental issues that are not concrete and not immediately rele-vant to the learners? Some have used case studies or success stories to help bridge this gap, making complex issues more relevant or concrete. More discussion and/or research are needed.

2. *Effectively using the stakeholder approach in programme development and evaluation:* The stakeholder approach is valued for reasons identified in Element B above. Multiple stakeholders often result in multiple interests, values and uses, which can sometimes lead to conflict. For example, a stakeholder team may have representatives from the agency, the school, and the community's primary industry and may strongly differ about the goals of the programme being developed. Further training and discussion is needed to help those trying to use the stakeholder approach handle conflict among stakeholders.

3. *Professional development for teachers and nonformal educators:* Although there are some good programmes to train pre-service and in-service teachers in environmental education, these programmes tend to be inconsistently available. Teachers often express misgivings about their ability to conduct environmental education programmes and with outdoor classroom management. Further, many agencies and organizations that have environmental education as part of their missions, but lack the expertise among their staff to develop and implement effective education programmes. Further discussion is needed to improve the quality and availability of professional development for pre-service and in-service teachers and for future non-formal environmental educators.

4. *Environmental education and education reform:* Environmental education has the potential to significantly

> improve the public education system. While initial studies are indicating that the goals of education reform can be effectively accomplished through environmental education, we do not know if environmental education is a necessary condition of improving education. For example, is using the environment as an integrating or motivating context better than using the arts as the context? Determining that environmental education is indeed a necessary component of improved education can help establish its place in the curriculum, making it less subject to funding priority shifts and more likely to be a focus in teacher training.

Most environmental education efforts target elementary and secondary students. As a result, important audiences - adults, people of color, low-income populations, senior citizens, and businesses, for example - are being missed or inadequately reached. Further research, discussion and training are needed in the area of knowing how to engage these audiences and how to adapt traditional teaching strategies to diverse communities and cultures.

8

Importance of Biodiversity Conservation

Much of human history has been written in terms of an ongoing struggle of "man against nature." The forces of nature – wild beasts, floods, pestilence, and disease — have been cast in the role of the enemy of humankind. To survive and prosper, we must conquer nature – kill the wild beasts, build dams to stop flooding, find medicines to fight disease, and use chemicals to control the pests. Humans have been locked in a life and death struggle against "Mother Nature." We've been winning battle after battle. But, we've been losing the war. Humans have killed so many "wild beasts" that non-human species are becoming extinct at an unprecedented rate – except in prehistoric times now labeled as global catastrophes. It's clear that humans cannot survive – nor might we want to survive – as the only living species on earth.

How many more species can we destroy before we lose more than we can afford to do without? How many more battles with Mother Nature can we afford to win? We have dammed so many streams the sediment that once replenished the topsoil of fertile farmland through periodic flooding now fills the reservoirs of lakes instead. Populations of fish and wildlife that once filled and surrounded free flowing streams, and fed the people of the land, have dwindled and disappeared. Floods may come less often now, but when nature really flexes its muscles, as in 1993 and 1996, nothing on earth can control the floods. How many more streams can we afford to dam? How many more battles with Mother Nature can we afford to win? We have wiped out plague after plague that has threatened humankind, and we now lead longer, presumably healthier, lives than ever before. But new, more sophisticated diseases always seem to come on the scene as soon as the old ones are brought under control. We may live longer, but that doesn't necessarily mean we are healthier.

Much of the medicine we take today is to treat the symptoms caused by the medicines we take. On average, we Americans spend more money for health care than we spend for food. How long can our new cures keep ahead of new diseases? How many more medical miracles can we afford? How many more battles with Mother Nature can we afford to win? We can quite easily kill most insects, diseases, weeds, and parasites using modern chemical pesticides. This has allowed us to realize the lower food prices brought about by a specialized, mechanized, standardized, industrialized agriculture.

But we still loose about the same percentage of our crops to pests as we did in earlier times. In addition, health concerns about pesticide residues in our food supplies and in our drinking water are on the rise. In addition, rural communities have withered and died and industrial agriculture has replaced the family farm.

Good paying jobs in the city are no longer there for people forced off the land. How many more pests can we afford to kill before we kill ourselves? How many more workers can we displace before we displace ourselves? How many more battles with Mother Nature can we afford to win? Every time we think we have won a battle, nature fights back. Nature always seems ready for the counterattack. And, people are beginning to lose faith in "man's" ability to ever conquer nature.

They are concerned about whether we can win the battle with the next flood, the next disease, or the next pest that we create with our efforts to control the last one. They are concerned with their own safety, health, and well being. But, they are concerned also about the sustainability of a human civilization that continues to live in conflict with nature.

They fear we cannot win our war against nature, because we are a part of nature – the very thing we are trying to destroy. They are searching for ways to find harmony with nature – to sustain the nature of which we are a part. A new paradigm or model for working and living in harmony with nature is arising under the conceptual umbrella of sustainability. Sustainable systems must be capable of meeting the needs of those of us of the present generation without compromising the ability of future generations to meet their needs as well.

In simple terms, sustainability means applying the Golden Rule across generations. It's about short run, self-interest – meeting our present needs; but it's also about long run, shared-interest – leaving equal or better opportunities for others both now and in the future. Sustainability requires that we find harmony between others and ourselves as well as between those of us of the present and those of the future. Sustainability requires that we find harmony.

The sustainable agriculture movement is but one small part of a far larger movement that is transforming the whole of human society. But a society that cannot feed itself quite simply is not sustainable. Human civilization is moving through a great transformation from the technology-based, industrial era of the past to a knowledge-based, "sustainable" era of the future. Agriculture is moving through a similar transition.

The industrial model of the past, and present, was based on the assumption that the welfare of people was in conflict with the welfare of nature. People had to harvest, mine, and otherwise exploit nature, including other people, to create more goods and services for consumption.

Human productivity is defined in terms of one's ability to produce goods and services that will be bought and consumed by others. Quality of life is viewed a consequence of consumption – something we can buy at Walmart or Disney World. The more we produce, the more we earn, the more we can consume, and the higher our quality of life. The more we can take from nature, and each other, the higher our quality of life.

The sustainable model is based on the assumption that people are multidimensional – that we are physical, mental, and spiritual beings. We have a mind and soul as well as a body. All three determine the quality of our life — what we think and what we feel as well as what we consume.

And, the three are as inseparable as the height, width, and length dimensions of a box. A life that lacks the physical, mental, or spiritual is not a life of quality, as an object that lacks a height, width, or length dimension is not a box. The industrial model has focused on the physical body, the self — getting more and more to consume. The sustainable model focuses on finding harmony among all three – the physical, mental, and spiritual — on leading a life of balance.

Spirituality is not synonymous with religion. Spirituality refers to a felt need to be in harmony with some higher unseen order of things – paraphrasing William James, a well-known religious philosopher. Religion, at its best, is simply one means of expressing one's spirituality.

Spirituality assumes a higher order to which humans must conform – if we are to find peace. Harmony cannot be achieved by changing the "order of things" to suit our preferences. Harmony comes only from changing our actions to conform to the "higher order." A life lived in harmony is its own reward.

A sustainable agriculture must be economically viable, socially responsible, and ecologically sound. The economic, social, and ecological are interrelated, and all are essential to sustainability. An agriculture that uses up or degrades its natural resource base, or pollutes the natural environment, eventually will lost its ability to produce. It's not sustainable.

An agriculture that isn't profitable, at least over time, will not allow its farmers to stay in business. It's not sustainable. An agriculture that fails to meet the needs of society, as producers and citizens as well as consumers, will not be sustained by society. It's not sustainable. A sustainable agriculture must be all three – ecologically sound, economically viable, and socially responsible. And the three must be in harmony.

Some see sustainability as an environmental issue. They are wrong. It is an environmental issue, but it is much more. Any system of production that attempts to conquer nature will create conflicts with nature, degrade its environment, and risk its long run sustainability. Industrial agriculture epitomizes a system of farming in conflict with nature. Sustainable farming systems must function in harmony with nature.

The fundamental purpose of agriculture is to convert solar energy into products for human food and fiber. Nature provides biological means of converting solar energy into living plants and animals. Nature provides means by which things come to life, protect themselves, grow to maturity, reproduce, and die to be recycled to support a future generation of life.

Agriculture attempts to tip the ecological balance in favor of humans relative to other species. But, if we attempt to tip the balance too far, too fast, we destroy the integrity of the natural system of which we are a part. A sustainable agriculture must be in harmony with nature. But, a sustainable agriculture also must be in harmony with people. Since people are a part of nature, with a basic nature of our own, a sustainable agriculture must also be in harmony with human nature. A socially sustainable agriculture must provide an adequate supply of food and fiber at a reasonable cost. Any system of agriculture that fails this test is not sustainable, no matter how ecologically sound it may be. But "man does not live by bread alone," and a socially responsible agriculture must contribute to a positive quality of life in other respects as well.

The industrial system of farming has destroyed the family farm as a social institution, has caused rural communities to wither and die, and has changed the social impact of agriculture on society in general from positive to negative. A sustainable agriculture must meet the food and fiber needs of people, but it cannot degrade or destroy opportunities for people to lead successful, productive lives in the process. A sustainable agriculture must be in harmony with our nature of being human.

Finally, a sustainable agriculture must be in harmony with the human economy. The greatest challenge to farming in ways that are ecologically sound and socially responsible is in finding ways to make such systems economically viable as well. Our current economy seems to favor systems that exploit their natural and human environment for short run gains.

Those who choose to protect the natural environment must sacrifice any economic opportunity that might result from exploiting it. Those who show concern for the well being of other people – workers, customers, or neighbors – must sacrifice any economic opportunity that might result from exploiting them. So it might seem that sustainability requires that one sacrifice some economic well being to achieve ecological and social sustainability.

Conventional thinking assumes the relationship among the environment, social, and economic wellbeing is a trade-off relationship – that one can have more of one only by sacrificing some of the others. However, this represents a highly materialistic worldview. If anyone gets more of something, then someone else must have less of it.

There is only some fixed quantity that must be allocated among competing ends. This materialistic worldview ignores the fact that we can gain satisfaction, for ourselves, right now, by doing things for others and by saving things for future generations – just because we know these are the right things to do. Our satisfaction is not dependent on realizing the expectations of some future personal rewards – the reward is embodied in the current action rather than the future outcome. There is inherent value in living and working in harmony. Getting more of one thing without having more of the others only creates imbalance and disharmony – making us worse off rather than better off.

However, the necessity for economic viability is a very real concern – even for those who pursue harmony rather than material wealth. If our endeavors are not economically viable, we lose the right to pursue those endeavors. But, how can a person make a living farming without degrading either the natural environment or the surrounding community?

Industrial farming sets the standard for dollar and cent costs of production – and industrial farming exploits its natural and human resource base to keep those costs to a minimum. How can a sustainable farmer compete? The answer is not to compete with industrial farming but to do something fundamentally different.

This something different includes letting nature do more of the work of production – working with nature rather than against it. Production costs may be competitive with, if not lower than, industrial systems if you let nature do enough of the work. Organic production methods, management intensive grazing, pastured pork and poultry, low-input farming — these are all systems that rely less on off-farm commercial inputs and more on one's ability to understand and work with nature. Industrial systems require uniformity and consistency, but nature is inherently diverse and dynamic. Harmony comes from matching what you produce and how you produce it to the unique ecological niche in which you produce. The greater the harmony the more of the work nature will be willing to do.

Finding harmony means reconnecting with the land. Wendell Berry puts it most succinctly in his book, What are People For, "...if agriculture is to remain productive, it must preserve the land and the fertility and ecological health of the land; the land, that is, must be used well. A further requirement, therefore, is that if the land is to be used well, the people who use it must know it well, must be highly motivated to use it well, must know how to use it well, must have time to use it well, and must be able to afford to use it well." Sustainable production is possible only if farmers have a harmonious relationship with the land – if they know it, care about it, know how to care for it, take time to care for it, and can afford to care for it – only if they love it.

Something different also means marketing in the niches – giving people what they really want rather than coercing or bribing them to take what you have for sale. The conventional wisdom is that niche markets are limited because individually they are small. The conventional wisdom is wrong. All consumer markets are niche markets, because they are made up of individuals, and we all want and need something a bit different. Industrial systems of mass production and mass distribution treat things as if they were pretty much the same.

The cost saving in industrial systems come from doing the same basic thing over and over again – producing uniform commodities in large volume. Niche marketing means giving people what they actually need and want – producing in harmony with the market. Finding harmony means reconnecting with people – as fellow human beings rather than as consumers, producers, or some other generic economic entity. Joel Salatin, a Virginia farmer and agripreneur, refers to this as "relationship marketing." When you have a relationship with your customers, they do not simply represent a market to be exploited to make a few more dollars. They are friends and neighbors that you care about and don't want to lose.

When your customers have a relationship with you, you are not just another supplier to be haggled down to the lowest possible price to save a few dollars. You are someone they care about and don't want to lose. When you know, care about, and have affection for each other, you have a relationship that creates value above and beyond market value. You are contributing directly to each other's quality of life. You are creating a harmony that arises only among people who love one another.

Neither land nor people can be sustained unless they are given the attention, care, and affection - the love — they need to survive, thrive, and prosper. The necessary attention, care, affection, and love come only from lives lived in harmony — among people and between people and nature. Finally, as more farmers and customers, sharing common concerns for ecological and social sustainability, develop relationships through the marketplace, their economic communities of interest will expand as well.

Customers will be willing to pay more and farmers will be willing to provide more because they are both getting more from the relationship than just money. Those who might attempt to exploit these new economic communities for short run gains - those motivated by economic value rather than ethical or moral values - are destined to find disappointment. Those who join in seeking balance among the economic, ecological, and social dimensions of their lives - among the physical, mental, and spiritual - will be rewarded. They are helping to create a new world in which people may learn to live in harmony with each other as well as in harmony with nature.

NEED OF CONSERVING BIODIVERSITY

There is a great concern over the loss of biological diversity, but at the same time few people know in any detail what is happening to the planet's diversity or can really say why they believe it is important. When it comes to conserving biodiversity, the definition that we use for it becomes extremely important. Simply defining it as "nature" is too nebulous, and makes deciding what actions to take difficult.

Besides, both a rainforest and a desert are part of nature, although their diversity is obviously very different. The definitions given in the introduction to this site, despite being formed by governments and international organizations, are fairly vague. Finer definitions have their own problems, though, as much of what one might consider diversity ends up not being included in these definitions. Is it even necessary to define biodiversity? Perhaps it is better to define it as needed for a particular area of study; as long as the definition and its limitations are kept in mind, this may be the most appropriate way of dealing with this problem. A major concern with this approach is that if the context is not kept in mind, later conclusions can be reached that are drastically different from those intended. For this section, the definition of biodiversity is deliberately left vague, as is appropriate for such a large issue. Biodiversity seems a concept that is better explained than defined.

Nature's Services to Humans

Nature and biodiversity provide services that we take for granted. Clean water to drink, clean air to breathe, soil for agriculture, the pollinating effect of many insects and much more is provided for us, but we tend not to pay much attention to these services. Because these services are largely invisible to us and difficult to give monetary values to, they tend to be given little weight when compared to development and policy decisions.

The value of provided services has been calculated for small areas, but it was only a few years ago that an attempt to calculate the value of these services over the entire world was performed. They estimated that these services are worth at least 33 trillion dollars, about twice the total economic output of the world! Although this estimate is crude and its exact value is debatable, it is very useful in pointing out just how important diversity is to us and how it should be taken more seriously in policy decisions than it is. Priorities for conservation are easier to decide upon if there is some basis for comparing, and these lists and estimates at least provide a way to make the comparisons.

Economic reasons

Nature provides huge direct and indirect economic benefits. In 1990 lumber cut in Canada (mostly from natural stands) had a value of $7.5 billion, while fishery catches were worth $1.5 billion. These values are for harvesting natural resources, and are limited by the natural productivity of nature. As can be seen by the recent crashes in the Atlantic fisheries, exceeding what nature can provide is economically dangerous, to say nothing of the ecological impacts.

Modern crops are extremely specialized strains of naturally occurring species, and the land they grow on is the result of the natural systems that they have displaced. Agriculture in Canada is worth $18 billion dollars per year and farm livestock contributes $11 billion dollars a year, but farming techniques reduce biodiversity by replacing natural communities with extremely artificial systems.

Recreation brings in even more money; benefits derived from Canada's natural areas such as national parks totaled an estimated $12 billion in expenditures and an additional $5 billion dollars in tax revenue in 1996. As ecotourism becomes more popular this value will increase in Canada, and internationally this source of income could be extremely important in the economies of developing nations.

Medicine

Out of the top 150 prescription drugs, 118 originally came from living creatures, mostly plants. Overall, seventy percent of pharmaceuticals now being used come from or are derived from natural products. Three substances that have been produced from the barks of tree species include: aspirin, from willow trees; quinine, which helps prevent malaria and is found in the bark of the quina tree; and taxol, a cancer-fighting drug derived from the bark of the Pacific yew tree. Digitalis, used to treat heart conditions, comes from the foxglove plant. The list goes on and on.

With the obvious health and financial importance of plant products, the destruction of biodiversity is a terrible waste. No one knows how many compounds in plants and animals can be used. Even if only a small fraction of plants and organisms produce useful medicinal products, it is a potential boon that we can't ignore and shouldn't destroy. Many pharmaceutical companies are currently engaged in bioprospecting, which consists of testing plant species for potentially useful compounds, sometimes signing agreements with national governments for permission. How many compounds are being lost before they are found is a mystery, but the number of potentially useful compounds found has been large.

Stability

Many parts of the natural world prevent or slow rapid change. One example would be forests, which prevent erosion and also prevent heavy rains from turning into floods. To some extent the climate is naturally held somewhat constant as well. This does not require diversity as much as nature; a forest with low diversity will prevent erosion as well as one with high diversity. Our current infrastructure is specialized enough to require this sort of stability.

The cost of repairing damage caused by flooding is enormous. Agricultural crops are specialized to grow extremely well, but only under specific conditions. If those conditions were to change, we would be forced to either move the crops to a region where those conditions exist or develop new strains of crops, both of which would be a sizeable drain on resources. Road, buildings, bridges, all are designed for a particular type of climate. It the climate changes, these structures will begin to crumble.

Aesthetic and philosophical importance

The long list of concrete benefits that diversity and nature provide should be enough to convince anyone of its importance, but there are also more esoteric, though no less important, reasons. Unfortunately, religions and philosophies don't say much about diversity and nature. One religious tradition that fairly directly mentions biodiversity is Judeo-Christianity, which promotes wise stewardship of the Earth.

Philosophies are usually focused on issues internal to ourselves, and don't truly deal with diversity either. Still, most religions and philosophies believe that destruction without just cause is wrong; as humans are responsible for most of the loss of diversity, we have a responsibility to stop doing harm and to repair as much of our damage as we can. Nature, and by extension diversity, also has an aesthetic quality. When people go hiking and canoeing it contributes to the economy in various ways but also enriches their lives. People experience nature in a way that goes beyond economics and also beyond nature's beauty.

How does one say exactly how beautiful a forest is, or how much one enjoyed a hike? Because this enjoyment cannot reasonably be quantified, it tends to be ignored in debates about conservation. Only the economic revenues associated with people getting to natural areas can be measured, and it's at best a poor replacement.

Human activities and their impacts

Humans, like all species, exploit their surroundings for the resources they need to survive. Our current exploitation of the world, however, is greater than those of most species, for three main reasons. The first is our technology. Like a few other species, we use tools, but the hand-held tools that we originally used could only alter extremely local conditions.

Today we are able to affect entire regions and our technology has progressed to the point where we can level mountains and control the flow of rivers, something that was simply impossible a relatively short while ago. We can now modify our world relatively easily and quickly. The second reason, our skyrocketing population, also increases the extent to which we modify the earth. It is estimated that the world's population reached one billion in 1804. By 1927 it was two billion, and it was three billion by 1960. It is currently six billion, and estimates for the year 2050 are for a global population of just under nine billion. With so many people, even minor activities per person will have major impacts when multiplied six billionfold.

Finally, consumption habits also have an affect; richer nations consume more resources and generate more waste than the less well-off. These three factors, acting together, are responsible for the changes that humans are bringing about on the planet. The major activities that are causing these changes are detailed below.

Fishing

In the past few decades, fishing fleets have grown enormously, and the UN Food and Agriculture Organization (FAO) estimates that the more than 3.5 million fishing vessels in the world hauled in 122 million tonnes of fish in 1997, six times what it had been in 1950. Here "fish" can mean both finfish (what we usually think of as fish) and shellfish.

Fisheries currently catch far more fish than the oceans can produce. Almost every major fishery in the world has seen its catch drop despite increasingly intense efforts, and many fisheries have collapsed entirely, the Grand Banks cod fishery being a noteworthy Canadian example. This overfishing isn't due to a lack of knowledge; as the New Scientist put it, "... for years, fisheries scientists have politely recommended to their governments that they should not let their fishing fleets catch quite so many fish next year. But every year... the answer comes back: we will let our fisherman catch far more fish than you scientists recommend."

Governments are tempted to keep fishing quotas high for short-term economic and political benefits, and are willing to heavily subsidize their fishing fleets. The FAO concluded that in 1992 fisheries were subsidized $50 billion dollars, almost as much as the $70 billion dollars of fish that they pulled from the sea. The result of this overfishing is that populations of economically important fish often become commercially extinct, reduced in numbers to the point where it is no longer viable to harvest them.

If fishing is stopped at this point, the fish species can hopefully avoid becoming biologically extinct. How long it takes the fish to return to commercially viable levels depends on the life cycle of the species, but several decades seems to be the minimum. When fish populations are drastically reduced, the ecological dynamics in the ocean change. Predators of the affected fish suffer, and other species may fill the role that the reduced species once did, making it unlikely or even impossible for that species to achieve its former numbers. If a species finds its role usurped by another species, it may be doomed to extinction even though it is no longer being actively fished.

Modern fishing techniques do more than just catch their intended species. Driftnets and longlines are notorious for killing other species, including seabirds and marine mammals. Bycatch, unwanted species that are caught along with the desired ones, makes up a quarter of the hauls that are harvested.

Most individuals caught as bycatch do not survive and their bodies are thrown back into the ocean. Seabed trawling destroys the structure and devastates the communities on the seabed, many of which take a long time to recover.

Aquaculture has risen in popularity in the past several years as a possible answer to declining fish stocks around the world. It consists of raising fish in enclosed areas, often simply fenced-off sections of natural waterways. Unfortunately, many of the most commercially important fish species are piscivorous, which can mean that three to five kilograms of other fish are needed to obtain one kilogram of the desired fish. This means that fisheries will be needed to feed the fisheries.

One concern with aquaculture is the excessive fertilization of the surrounding waters by feces and uneaten food. Another is the inevitable escape of the farmed animals. These escaped fish can be an invasive species, displacing native fish and altering the ecosystem. If the escaped fish are the same species as locally-occurring fish, they may interbreed with them, introducing new genetic traits that may harm the native population.

Freshwater sport fishing may also cause problems through overfishing and the introduction of commercially desirable fish to lakes and rivers that they are not native to. This has happened throughout Canada and the world. The Nile Perch is a dramatic example of the possible results: introduced to Lake Victoria in 1954 as a game fish, the population exploded in the 1980s. Other fish species in the lake were its prey; 65% of them eventually went extinct and the ecology of the lake was radically changed.

Forestry

Forestry is similar to fishing, in that it is the harvesting of a natural growing resource. A major difference is that in fisheries the amount of fish caught is the number of concern, while in forestry the numbers refer to the area logged. Forestry is the removal of individuals but also the destruction of habitat which the trees create. The most common method of harvesting in forestry is clearcutting, in which entire stands of trees are cut down at the same time.

This is much more destructive than the selective cuttings that can be employed instead. Out of the million hectares of Canadian forests harvested in 1996, 86% were clearcut, with less than half of that being reseeded or planted with seedings. Biological diversity obviously drops instantly when everything is cut, and it takes decades for a new forest to grow back to the same size and density as the previous forest had. Even when the trees are the same size as those that were originally cut, the forest that has grown will have lower biodiversity than the original forest; the older the original forest, the more the new forest will be lacking.

Regrowth, especially from treeplanting, is typically uniform in density and type of tree, which is unnatural. This uniformity in a forest also help reduce diversity as there different environments are no longer present for different species.

In addition to the drop in diversity clearcut regions have much of their nutrient-rich topsoil swept away by rain and wind, and the nutrients often end up in rivers, overloading the river with nutrients in a process called eutrophication. Forests also act to absorb rainflow; without them, floods are more common. Even when strips or sections of forest are left uncut instead of clearcutting, the results are far from ideal.

The edges of the uncut fragments of forest suffer from wind and the area becomes drier. While this happens in normal forests as well, it only happens to the edges of the forest. The fragments left after logging are largely edge, and much of the total forest left begins to dry out. Species that need large areas, including large mammals such as bears, cannot live in the small fragments. Roads, including forestry roads, have much the same effect, effectively cutting the forest into fragments for them.

Urbanization and development

Statistics Canada reported that 78% of Canada's population lived in urban areas in 1996. Urban areas are relatively small, with high population densities, though the spread of urban sprawl, largely through suburbs, has made them much larger in the past few decades. Cities produce large amounts of pollution, which can be problem to those living downwind and downstream, and also influence local climates.

Because cities began in areas with good farmland, their growth ends up paving over the former farms. The inevitable network of roads, railways and satellite communities end up fragmenting natural habitats and putting pressure on the species in the area. The Mixedwood Plains ecozone includes half of Canada's population in the Quebec City-Windsor corridor. This ecozone is also extremely rich in species, though the development of the region has put such a strain on natural communities that half of Canada's endangered species are found here.

Agriculture

Agriculture is the major farming activity, taking up much of the land in the south of Canada. The Prairies ecozone has almost entirely been taken over by agriculture, with only 13% of the shortgrass prairie, 19% of the mixedgrass prairie, and virtually none of the tallgrass prairie community remaining. With so little remaining original land, many Prairie species are threatened.

In contrast, many pest species are introduced to the region and flourish with the large expanses of a single food source. Agriculture's scale means not only that large areas are directly affected, but that local and even regional climates can be affected. The draining of water from rivers and watersheds for irrigation leads to drier natural habitats. Those rivers that receive runoff from farmland are often poisoned by excessive nutrients and pesticides.

Agriculture also leads to soil erosion, both through rainfall and wind. This soil can damage the aquatic ecosystems it ends up in, and the loss of nutrients can result in productive farmland becoming barren. In comparison to arable farming, livestock farming has a relatively minor impact, though intensive livestock production results in local problems, with fecal matter pollution of waterways often becoming a major issue.

Industry

As a wide term covering not only manufacturing, but also other activities such as mining, dams and power plants, industry as a whole affects huge areas of the country. Some effects, like mining, are fairly small-scale, while dams can affect enormous areas. Dams disrupt water flow downriver while flooding large areas upriver. This flooding often releases mercury from decaying plants into the water. Pollution is produced from many activities and comes in many forms: heat pollution, chemical pollution of water and soil, atmospheric pollution that causes acid rain, and more. In older economic models pollution was an "externality," outside of the model and therefore ignored. This thinking is happily now changing.

Probably the most drastic effect is climate change, usually referred to as global warming. The greenhouse gases released by industry as well as by vehicles is changing the climate of the entire planet. Exactly what the changes will be is still unknown, but our current set of constructions and farms are not easily moved to new locations, so most any change would have deleterious effects. A larger effect than changing the weather on the entire planet is hard to imagine, but it is being done and no one knows where it will take us.

CONSERVATON PRIORITIES

Knowing how important diversity is and that our activities are having detrimental effects upon it leads to the inescapable conclusion that it must be protected. Agreeing that it needs to be protected is simple enough, but deciding how to protect it and what to protect is much more complicated. This page briefly covers the historical thinking on conservation and some of the ideas and priorities of current conservation action. Details on the actual acts and organizations are found in the Legislation section of this site.

A focus on species

Originally, conservation was ignored in what was considered to be a world of infinite resources. Originally, land that was set aside was for economic reasons; the creation of Banff National Park in 1885 was not done to protect wildlife but to provide a vacation spa and wilderness recreation park. Early efforts at conservation were focused on protecting species. Not all endangered species were protected, though; at first only economically important species were given much weight, in part because they were the species whose decline was worrisome and in part because the extinction of species thought of as pests was still welcomed. In time, though, species that didn't have obvious commercial benefits for humans were also protected. There is a natural tendency to think of conservation in terms of species.

The loss of a species is something that is easier to grasp and more tangible than the loss of genetic diversity or an ecosystem, and many endangered species are photogenic enough to evoke an immediate emotional response. Even scientifically, species are easier to work with than genetics or ecosystems (see the Theory section for why this is), which leads to species getting the lion's share of attention even from conservation biologists.

Protecting ecosystems

Up until fairly recently protection focused almost exclusively on the species itself. Habitat protection originally had little to do with species protection, as the view was still that the environment was limitless and the consequences of human activities on it minor. Species that we specifically harvest might be endangered, but the systems they were a part of weren't considered to be at risk. Only with the creation of the Canadian Wildlife Service in 1973 were ecosystems being truly protected by law.

Trying to save species individually is not very effective; there are over three hundred threatened and endangered Canadian species and populations on COSEWIC's list, and separate efforts to save each of them would be wasteful. Protecting the habitat of these species makes much more sense, as there is little chance of them going extinct in their natural environment once it is safe. In addition to saving those already endangered species, this approach helps prevent other species who share the same habitat from becoming endangered and preserves the ecological integrity of the protected area. Protecting areas saves all levels of diversity. Efforts were made to protect systems, but not until "Our Common Future," the 1987 report of the UN's World Commission on Environment and Development was released, was the idea taken very seriously. The report was enormously influential, and its emphasis on habitat protection as a better means to protect species led to the widespread adoption of that practice.

Deciding what gets protected

Ideally all biological diversity would be protected, but this isn't likely to happen any time soon. Rather than randomly conserving patches of habitat, what gets protected is a mix of systems and species that are in immediate danger or that have special characteristics. Many countries have passed legislation that makes it difficult to destroy the habitat or to kill members of endangered species, and legislation that likewise protects endangered ecosystems is also becoming more common.

Species that are threatened in Canada are designated by COSEWIC; unfortunately, Canada currently has no endangered species act to consistently protect endangered species, and COSEWIC's list of threatened and endangered species has no binding legal implications. A key special characteristic for an area is to have especially high numbers of species. These areas are known as "biodiversity hotspots" and are generally found in the tropics, though Canada has hotspots as well.

Globally, it has been estimated that almost half of all higher plant species and over a third of amphibian, reptile, mammal and bird species can be found in 25 hotspots that take up only 1.4% of the land of the planet. Naturally, this does not mean that most of the natural landscapes of the world can be destroyed without any ill effects resulting, but it does mean that a large proportion of species can be protected in a relatively small proportion of the world's surface. Areas that perform important ecosystem functions in relation to their size, such as the water filtering activities of wetlands, are also special areas that should be protected. Keystone species (see the Theory section) are examples of species with special characteristics; similar to the wetlands just described, they have a larger impact on their system than would be expected by their numbers. When it comes time to decide if certain species or areas should be protected, the decisions made unfortunately often end up resembling popularity contests.

Attractive species and areas get more attention and arouse more passion than their less attractive cousins. Endangered insects aren't held in the same regard as endangered mammals, and picturesque landscapes are defended with more vigour than marshes. This phenomenon is so widely recognized that a term has been coined for these attractive species: charismatic megafauna. What all this means is that the focus of conservation efforts is diverted from species and areas that may be more important or threatened to those that are simply beautiful. Given how close to extinction many species are, this is a truly unfortunate.

CONSERVATION STRATEGIES

Ecological degradation and its corollary - biodiversity loss - pose a serious threat to development. 'Ecologically destructive economic activities are inefficient not merely because of the resulting resource misallocation but also beçause of the scale of activity levels; excessive in relation to the limited availability of natural capital when the latter is complementary to human-made capital'. In order to bring about sustainable resource conservation and management, it is essential to adopt several different approaches for managing our forests and biodiversity.

Future efforts for conservation and management of our natural resources must derive from a set of clear objectives, mechanisms for action, and commitment from all stakeholders.

Apart from this, halting the process of degradation and species loss requires specialized solutions and an understanding of ecological processes. Protecting biodiversity does not merely involve setting aside chunks of area as reserves. Instead, all the ecological processes that have maintained the area's biodiversity such as predation, pollination, parasitism, seed dispersal, and herbivory, involving complex interactions between several species of plants and animal needs to be ensured. This, however, is possible only if reserves are large enough to maintain these processes and some of the other crucial links in the web of life. For example the Barro Colorado island, is a 1600 ha island in Gatun Lake, an artificial impoundment in the Panama canal. This island is a biological field station of the Smithsonian Institution in Panama and a research preserve. Researchers have noticed that several common species of birds were disappearing rapidly and mysteriously for no clear reasons as to the causes, while the same species were common on the nearby mainland.

Additionally, several large predators including jaguars and pumas had gone extinct early in the island's history. Biotic factors could be ruled out, because the island was uninhabited except for a few biologists. Interestingly, the only similarity between the birds going extinct was that they were large bodied and either foraged or nested near the ground. Scientific research suggests that the small, fragmented area of the island was inadequate to sustain large predators, which were the first to go extinct.

This led to population increases of their prey species, which had earlier been kept in balance by the top predators. These meso-predators preyed on the eggs and young of ground nesting birds and their increase in numbers was sufficient to wipe out populations of birds. Thus forest fragmentation led to an unbalancing of ecological processes and the extinction of ground nesting bird species.

There is also the need for greater involvement of communities, and for models which decentralize of management and conservation roles and responsibilities. As of now, there are still major lacunae in information resources pertaining to forests, biodiversity - flora and fauna, causative factors for their degradation, and major threats. The available data is alarmingly inadequate to provide a lucid picture of the current status and ongoing losses/gains. More importantly, laws and policies governing natural resources are still not sufficient enough to tackle the scale of the problem, and these insufficiencies have not been addressed with a sense of urgency. In this section, we provide some indicators of the biological policy, technological, and institutional issues that will help mitigate the disturbingly accelerating biodiversity loss.

Maintaining viable populations of species, whether plant or animal, is a crucial factor in biodiversity conservation and this requires the appropriate conservation of important ecosystems and habitats. Currently, the country has 88 national parks, and 490 sanctuaries. In 1988, Rodgers and Panwar conducted a comprehensive study in which they drew up plans for a protected area network to cover the range of biological diversity in the country. They suggested that the percentage of the country's area under the protected area network, which was then only 3.3%, be enhanced to 4.6%.

The recent update of the Rodgers and Panwar report suggests that the area under parks and sanctuaries be increased to 160 National Parks and 698 sanctuaries accounting for 5.69 % of the country's geographical total. This coverage will provide a 'better distribution of protected areas with less gaps in the protection of biogeographic zones, biomes and species and fewer spatial or geographic gaps in the pattern of PA coverage'. Currently, the protected area network does not adequately cover some important biomes and mammal species of conservation significance.

Conservation strategies are urgently needed for the protection of species and ecosystems, involving a mix of in situ and ex situ strategies. Some of the steps in such a policy include the following.

Population surveys and assessments and database creation

Adequate data on species diversity, populations, location and extent of habitat, major threats to different species, etc. , and changes in these aspects over time are not available to design a proper strategy for conservation. Given our extensive diversity, ecological surveys and taxonomic investigations need to be intensified, particularly for plants and insects. For conducting ecological studies, species for such studies can be prioritized including keystone species, large mammals, migratory species, etc.

The country's wildlife institutions need to network and coordinate their activities so that priority issues and areas are identified. The Ministry of Environment and Forests (MoEF) through the Botanical Surveys of India and the Zoological Survey of India could play a guiding role by preparing a list of priority issues and areas for circulation to relevant institutions, based on a countrywide consultation of experts. Funding for these prioritized projects could be stepped up to ensure that research focuses on these issues. The MoEF must set up a database for the country as a whole.

Mapping of forest types, protected areas, and natural forests

It is important to generate maps of the protected areas of the country showing their contiguity with the existing reserve and protected forests. This will provide a way for determining possible corridors, habitat contiguity, and buffer zones and facilitate biodiversity conservation. Further, vegetation mapping according to forest types needs to be done for the entire country. The Forest Survey of India data need to show the disaggregated changes in area according to forest types and natural forest areas. Current data on canopy densities make it difficult to estimate the changes in area under dense, natural, or near-natural forests.

Improved protection efforts and a landscape approach to conservation

Owing to habitat fragmentation and consequent losses suffered by different populations, there is need for ensuring the safety of the biodiversity lying outside our protected areas. Population viability analyses for different species have revealed that the loss of even a single individual from a small isolated population could adversely affect the population structure and viability and push many species towards extinction.

The need of the hour is a landscape approach to conservation where protected and non-protected areas are integrated through significant protection measures initiated at both the state and local community levels. This will include the following activities.

— Mapping the distribution of habitat types in the region as types of landscape elements (LSE) with the help of satellite imagery along with field surveys

— Establishing association of groups of species with different types of LSEs on the basis of field surveys

— Assessing rates of transformations of LSE types with the help of satellite imagery of earlier years, official records, and oral histories

— Assessing the threats to different species as a result of ongoing landscape changes and other causes like commercial harvests

— Assigning conservation priorities to species on the basis of threats to their populations, rarity, endemism, and taxonomic distinctiveness

— Assigning conservation priorities to different types of habitats or LSEs on the basis of richness and conservation significance of the threatened species they harbour

In situ conservation

Good management of the extant populations in the wild is essential for their survival. This includes facilitating gene flow through the creation of corridors, introduction of new genetic stock, and translocation of animals. While habitat protection and corridor creation may be possible, large-scale manipulations of the extant populations, e.g. through translocations, however, are yet to catch on in India because of financial and logistical problems. There are some exceptions such as the proposed transfer of some lions from Gir to Kuno Palpur in Madhya Pradesh.

Regular population-habitat viability and risk simulations

Computer models for regular population and habitat viability assessments should be generated on the basis of newly identified threats, population status, and other relevant research. These models can provide estimates for the survival of these populations for the next 100 years while also indicating the various steps needed for improving the overall conservation status of the species. This would prove indispensable for saving many threatened and endangered species.

Captive breeding and species reintroduction

Captive breeding aims at maintaining viable and healthy genetic captive stocks in conservation facilities and is meant to supplement in situ initiatives. Captive breeding can provide animals for possible reintroduction to the wild at a later stage or for supplementing current populations with new stock. In situ measures, however, are always preferred, since in most cases it is cheaper to protect populations in their natural habitat than to reintroduce captive-bred ones.

Dudwa rhino reintroduction

The Dudwa forests were home to the one horned rhino a century and half ago. However due to rampant poaching for its valuable horn and for game hunting, it was wiped out from the area by the late 19th century. Rhinos were successfully reintroduced to Dudwa on 1 April, 1984 following a systematic reintroduction effort of captive bred stock. Suitable habitats were first earmarked prior to their reintroduction. About 27 km2 of grasslands and open forests with perennial source of water was earmarked as the rhino-reintroduction area and two monitoring stations established. Currently there are seven rhinos breeding successfully - 4 adult females, 1 adult male, and 2 sub-adult males.

Some of the steps involved in ex-situ conservation include the following.

- establishing minimum target population goals to provide for maintenance of captive genetic diversity for at least the next 100 years
- distributing founders through the various captive breeding programmes
- compiling animal husbandry programmes for circulation to all breeding facilities, and
- implement an overall plan that contributes to the objectives of maintaining viable captive populations across the globe - a strategy known as the Global Animal Survival Plan (GASP).

Because of limitations of space, finances, and facilities in the institutions that undertake captive breeding, species prioritization is a primary concern. An overwhelming 91% of animals kept in Indian zoos are non-threatened, yet take up much of the space and resources of zoos. Zoos in India may need to restrict their efforts to a few species that can benefit from captive breeding initiatives, such as small-bodied species of Chiroptera, Rodentia, and Insectivora. These make up 60% of mammalian taxa in the country and are easier to reintroduce than larger mammals. Instead, mini zoos and deer parks can act as a sink for the surplus, hybrid, aged, and infirm animals while tne larger zoos can focus on serious captive breeding.

Preservation plots

A number of states, eg. Uttar Pradesh and Uttaranchal, have forest preservation plots. These are important means for conserving and protecting important floral species as well as for assessing ecological changes occurring in such areas over a period of time. These plots need to be demarcated and actively maintained.

The initial success of Project Tiger was eroded by an increased demand for some body parts of a tiger, especially bones, leading to the involvement of illegal traffickers. Though India has made great efforts to save the tiger, the relatively recent threat of wildlife trade would need to be tackled through better enforcement and effective implementation of the Wildlife Protection Act. To tighten the enforcement of the existing wildlife law at least six major steps are needed. These are as follows.

— Setting up of a central task force to be designated as the directorate of prevention of crime against wildlife. This will have an intelligence unit, a legal cell, an investigation wing, and an operation cell to carry out undercover operations.

— Creation of special courts in each state for adjudicating on wildlife crimes

— Creation of a central wildlife crime databank to collect and analyse data on wildlife trade

— Activating state forest vigilance cells and creating a legal cell within each sate forest department.

— Formation of an enforcement cell by the state chief wildlife wardens.

Project Tiger—A success in species conservation

Tiger populations declined drastically from estimates of 40000 at the turn of the century to 1800 by the 1970s. This led in 1973 to the initiation of Project Tiger with the objective of conserving and rescuing this species from annihilation. Twenty-three tiger reserves were set up along with the imposition of a total ban on hunting and trading in tiger products at the national and international levels and the implementation of habitat improvement and anti-poaching measures. Between 1973 to 1989, the species showed a marked recovery resulting in an increase in numbers to more than 4000 by 1989.

Information networking

There are a multitude of agencies, both government-controlled and private, involved in the generation and dissemination of data. In the absence of a system/mechanism (state-sponsored or otherwise), for effective sourcing and pooling of information, there is often colossal wastage of money and efforts in recreating such data. Promoting networking and sharing of information is essential for an informed and inexpensive approach to biodiversity conservation.

Geographical information systems and remote sensing in planning and monitoring

Utilization of Geographical Information Systems (GIS) and remote sensing could help determine the rates, causes, and scale of biodiversity loss. These systems blend information obtained from various sources such as Survey of India topographic sheets, vegetation maps, remote sensing imagery, and other archival material to provide a picture of the state and extent of resource loss over time. Information on deforestation and land-use change can be integrated with data on the distribution of biodiversity and existing information on soils, topography, climate, etc. to obtain a comprehensive picture. GIS must be used more extensively as a tool in policy and landscape level planning.

The number of parks and sanctuaries that can be increased in India is very limited given the hardships they impose on the local people. At the same time, the protected area network is inadequate in protecting ecologically important and fragile ecosystems such as wetlands, mangroves, and grasslands that lie outside such protected areas (PAs). Possible viable solutions include the following.

Creation of new conservation reserves Create new types of legally recognized reserves where sustainable utilization and community involvement is the norm. Currently only national parks and sanctuaries are legal entities, which were created largely on the exclusionary principle.

Community reserves

Community reserves will protect landscapes, ecosystems, and species traditionally or culturally conserved by local communities. These reserves will be limited to private and community land, not government owned areas

People protecting pelicans: an example of community conservation in India

Kokkare Bellur is a village situated in Mandya District of Karnataka, India. For generations, storks and pelicans have been coming here and roosting on the trees in the village for six months. They breed here, feed in the water bodies spread within a distance of a few kilometers and then fly away to their summer grounds. The villagers consider them a good omen and harbinger of good rain and protected their habitat. Villagers have also established an orphanage for injured birds. This area would prove to be an excellent community managed reserve.

In Pilibhit district of Uttar Pradesh lies a 1 ha village pond, which is protected by the local people and is home to several migratory waterfowl. The people have traditionally protected the birds and there is a community-enforced ban on hunting and poaching of birds from the pond. Although small in area, this pond provides an example of traditional respect for wildlife through community enforced bans on hunting and poaching. Further, because of protection offered to the birds here, this pond teems with birdlife in the winter. Huge signboards listing birds seen in this area indicate that this pond hosts a number of migratory waterfowl.

Conservation reserves

Conservation reserves can either be additional to the current protected areas system and/or may act as a buffer around the existing ones. Local communities could help in managing such areas to meet their bonafide livelihood needs, perhaps through ecotourism. While the inclusion of these categories within the Wildlife (Protection) Act is currently on the anvil, it must be expedited.

Conservation forestry

Since a large proportion of biodiversity occurs outside the network of protected areas, considerations of conservation outside protected areas must become an integral part of forest management. Making divisional working plans, which govern forest management in India more sensitive to issues of biodiversity conservation can achieve this objective since working plans govern forest management in India. Working plans largely provide silvicultural operations for forest divisions and their biodiversity concerns are limited. For example, they prescribe the removal of all dead, dying, and diseased trees which, however, provide excellent habitats for birds that nest in cavities. A new working plan code that is being drafted to guide the development of working plans across the country should incorporate the following biodiversity concerns.

— Biannual census of large mammals using scientific census techniques and also of water birds for important wetlands

— Updated information on vegetation communities and floral inventories with cooperation of Botanical Survey of India, Zoological Survey of India, universities, etc.

— Identification of important habitats and their management

— Compartment histories inclusive of all wildlife data

— Simple regular monitoring and maintaining records of sightings and observation of flora and fauna by forest guards and foresters.

Each state must identify forests, grasslands, wetlands, and other areas of importance for biodiversity and include those lying on forest land within protection working circles (where no silvicultural working is allowed). These areas can also be designated as wildlife ranges where wildlife range officers report to the territorial divisional forest officers. This will ensure that biodiversity conservation is not merely restricted to the wildlife wing of the forest departments but becomes a regular feature of forest management.

Community-oriented approaches

An important factor contributing to the endangered status of many species is anthropogenic activity. Populations dependent on local forests also contribute to species endangerment by over-exploiting forest produce in the absence of livelihood alternatives. There is need for involving people and their knowledge base for protection and management of biodiversity. TERI, Vivekananda Girijana Kalayana Kendra, (VGKK) and Ashoka Trust for Research in Ecology and Environment (ATREE), designed a project to increase the economic stake of the Soligas in conserving their biotic resources and their capacity to ensure the ecological sustainability of these resources and the larger ecosystem. Therefore, local communities who influence conservation, management, and utilization of biodiversity are major stakeholders in its conservation.

In areas where people are to be involved, incentives for their participation must be identified. Maintenance of protected areas requires long-term strategies to divert biotic pressures. For this, the spread and intensity of activities on eco-development projects need to be increased.

Poverty, dependency on forests, and erosion of biodiversity are closely intertwined. Therefore, the creation of a forest area development agency to operate along the lines of the District Rural Development Agency, headed by the forest department is a very progressive step. The government needs to expedite the formation of this agency. Further, the chief development officers in forest areas need to be from the forest department, a step that has already been taken in Andhra Pradesh. This will ensure that rural development assistance is provided directly to forest villages.

Eco-tourism and recreation forestry are being tried as an income-earning options for local communities. These need to be formalized and included in the relevant policies, to be preceded by in-depth studies to determine the feasibility and the costs and benefits of such projects for all stakeholders. In order to conserve forests and to offer incentives to local communities and private parties, development of forests for recreation purposes such as wildlife watching, adventure tourism, nature trails, hiking, camping, angling, and water sports can be considered. This will provide monetary returns to the forest department, while ensuring that biodiverse patches are protected with support of the local community. Such use of forests can be promoted near sanctuaries and national parks, where visits to the protected areas are combined with recreation forestry, or near important religious or other tourism areas. An memorandum of understanding can be signed with private parties or local communities with adequate safeguards against degradation and misuse of the area.

Community biodiversity registers must be developed before issues of ownership of resources and equitable sharing of benefits are sorted out clearly. These registers will help in organizing relevant information at the micro-level on patterns of utilization, conservation, status, and management that would form the basis of identifying sustainable livelihood patterns. Bioprospecting projects are possible. Such partnerships in India, however, are still often exploitative. Instead, the government of

India needs to issue clear guidelines for managing bioprospecting agreements.

Bioprospecting involving local communities

The Kani-Tropical Botanic Garden and Research Institute (TBGRI). The TBGRI developed a drug Jeevani from Trichopus zeylanicus, a plant whose fruits were traditionally eaten by the Kani tribals to provide energy and agility. A licence to manufacture this drug was given to Arya Vaidya Pharmacy (Coimbatore) Ltd for a period of 7 years for Rs 1 million of which the tribals were to receive 50% of the licence fee as well as 50% of the royalty obtained by TBGRI on the sale of the drug. In December 1987, this plant was discovered when scientists of TBGRI on a bioprospecting trip to the Western Ghats, noticed that their tribal guides gained energy after eating the fruits of this plant. The leaves of this plant with some other ingredients was later developed into Jeevani. This agreement received criticism for its inequitable nature because of the lack of involvement of the entire Kani community, and failure to take permission from the Kani medical practitioners who are the guardians of this knowledge.

In protected areas there can be several ways of involving local communities or at least mitigating some of their hardships as under:

— reserving up to 50% of available posts (e.g. wildlife guards and forest watchers) for members of local communities,

— employing them in collecting snake venom, building anti-poaching awareness groups, and other local activities,

— capturing and training elephants who devastate standing crops to reduce conflicts, and

— initiating timely schemes of compensation for those who lose their cattle to wildlife

Harnessing voluntary action

Some voluntary, field based organizations and non-governmental organizations (NGOs) have the flexibility to develop, test, and carry out innovative approaches to working with communities, especially women and the poor. They have a role in policy advocacy, information gathering, and applied research. They have the ability to raise public awareness and provide technical assistance and other extension activities. NGOs could complement or supplement government efforts and also play the very important role of environmental watchdogs capable of influencing public policies and programmes.

Involvement of the private sector

The private sector needs to be involved much more in such biodiversity projects as the development of forest areas for tourism or in the setting up of nature parks and interpretation centres or in bioprospecting agreements. Such involvement, however, in all cases must ensure priority to local communities.

Nature and interpretation parks

Cities and towns need to have nature parks combining botanical gardens with interpretation centres for conservation education through film shows, bird and butterfly watching, dioramas, nature trails and activities, some live animal exhibits such as insectariums, reptile exhibits, butterfly parks. Such a centre would need to be staffed by zoologists, botanists, and educationists. In order to make such a venture profitable, private participation may be considered.

9

Role of School in Environmental Conservation and Sustainable Development

The development of social imperatives in relation to sustainable development now has considerable momentum and the phrase is becoming rooted in the discourse of UN agencies, national governments, business, the professions, educational institutions, and NGOs. However, Dobson noted finding over 300 definitions, and disputation continues with rival meanings being used as competing rhetorical currencies in a market for which, and whose, worldviews will best save the planet.

Pawley describes phrases such as sustainable development as textbook examples of political fudge-words that combine opposite positions by proposing the authority of a third, while Stables has described them, along with phrases such as equality of opportunity and global citizenship, as paradoxical compound policy slogans. In education, currently, there is a tendency towards prepositional forms: ie, education for sustainable development. Although this is likely to owe something to pre-existing terminology (viz., education for the environment), its use may also be programmatic for particular social purposes. As Jickling and Spork note:

> ... programmatic definitions ... go further than prescribing a particular meaning. They may be used to express

> particular moral or practical choices – to advance an agenda.

In England, two main aims are set for the school curriculum. These are:

> The school curriculum should pass on enduring values ... and help [learners] to be responsible and caring citizens capable of contributing to a just society. It should develop their awareness and understanding of, and respect for, the environments in which they live, and secure their commitment to sustainable development at a personal, local, national and global level.

Such a fundamental social goal as sustainable development has potentially considerable implications for all aspects of society and raises question about the balance between schools' need to help implement government policies and their need to mediate them. Such policies will apply to schools as institutions, as well as to curricula, and different responsibilities apply. It will be difficult for schools to avoid the effects of some sustainable development policies (eg, legislation on waste disposal) but, even with a mandated national curriculum, schools may still choose to question the policy. This is not to argue that such policy should be opposed through the curriculum; rather it is to acknowledge the choice, and the need to exercise this both consciously and conscientiously.

SUPPORTING EDUCATION FOR SUSTAINABLE DEVELOPMENT

Debates in the literature, and recent editions of Environmental Education Research and the Canadian Journal of Environmental Education, show the growth of the sustainable development discourse and particular tendencies. Hopkins comments that education should be seen as a primary tool in the critical endeavour of attaining a sustainable future, and the World Wildlife Fund-UK's school resource, *Lessons in Life* notes:

> We have a responsibility to help young people to understand the reasons for sustainable development, and

> to develop the knowledge, skills and values on which to base their future decisions and actions.

Such tendentious and determinist language is not uncommon within the literature.

More appropriately, and more democratically perhaps, we ought to want schools to help learners develop critical understandings of sustainable development, and help them achieve levels of critical environmental literacy that will enable them to develop and continually adapt their own understandings and make up their own minds as to how (and whether) to change the ways that they live. It would be more ethical, and more useful, were we to acknowledge that the purpose of education in relation to sustainable development was to explore the concept and its implications, tolerating different views in this process, rather than to persuade people to accept it, whatever its implications.

But this would sit uncomfortably under an education for sustainable development banner where the for represents an instrumental view of education in the service of government in pursuit of the goal of sustainable development, and a denial of the essence of education within a liberal democracy which aims to aid learners to think for themselves.

Foster argues that:

> The relation between education and sustainability cannot be an external, still less an instrumental one. ... Learning to understand the natural world and the human place in it can only be an active process through which our sense of what counts as going with the grain of nature is continually constituted and recreated. This process cannot have its agenda set to subserve sustainability criteria which it actually makes meaningful. The policy discourse, parameters and indices of operational sustainability are heuristics, and the conditions for deploying them intelligently are at one and the same time the condition for a genuinely learning, and for a deeply sustainability, society.

Concern about the dangers of schools doing a government's bidding, is hardly new. Neither is the notion that the responsibility which schools and teachers have should be to society, as a means of aiding its development, rather than to transient government. So what should the responsibility of schools be towards sustainable development? What are schools for?

Curriculum and Liberty

In a 1998 on-line colloquium on the future of environmental education in a postmodern world, Sauvé critiqued moves to reshape education such that sustainable development is seen as the ultimate goal of human development with education as instrumental to this end, noting modernism's tendency to develop universalizing socio-political theories and socio-economic organizing principles, namely capitalism and communism, which tend to convey universal values. Clearly, humanist thought arising from the Enlightenment has effected both capitalist and socialist development. Equally clearly, many such modernist projects set out to constrain and shape the liberty of the individual in order to realize their social and political goals.

Of course, even in relatively liberal social democracies, there are constraints on aspects of individual liberty to protect other liberties, and this is done largely with majority compliance. Liberal democratic governments run into civil liberties difficulties when they criminalize activities which their citizens (a significant minority, at least) regard as quite proper, or act to achieve social goals which command little respect. Such approaches are common where governments have strong social agendas. In communist societies, the freedom of the individual was routinely curtailed in order to achieve revolutionary social ends, with schools being used instrumentally in this. We dwell on these issues because liberty is a word which is effectively missing from the sustainable development, education discourse, where value concepts of "justice" (both social and ecological) and "equality" (both inter- and intra-generational, and sometimes inter-species) dominate.

This notion of liberty grew out of Enlightenment thinking and might be thought a particularly western notion, with cultural limitations, but none of this invalidates its importance as an idea, or reduces its ideological significance. Ignoring liberty lends credence to the idea that justice and equality can each be maximised at no cost to other values. However, the concepts of justice, equality and liberty are incommensurate, and to claim otherwise is to mislead. It is a point Ross also makes, quoting Pepper, who promises that a future green socialism, "... will be less prone to totalitarianism than some previous 'socialisms', though it will still entail sacrifice of some extant liberal 'freedoms' ... but this may be no bad thing." Although this is a view which Dworkin would not entirely share.

Liberty, of course, tends to be exercised most (but not always extended) by those with the most power in society, but herein lies the dilemma: should societies reduce available freedoms on the hypothesis that more can then share, more equally, whatever is left, (seeing equality as the dominant value), or should they extend freedoms more widely through educational, legislative, economic, and other levers (seeing liberty as the higher value)? Education has a crucial, if quite different role, in each of these strategies: between a voluntary approach, where people make their own decisions, and a compulsory approach where non-compliance is subject to legal sanction. The implications for state-funded schools in England of having a legally mandated curriculum aim of securing pupils' "commitment to sustainable development at a personal, local, national and global level," are unknown.

If the purpose of education isn't to effect some external-evolved social plan, as strongly criticized by Jensen and Schnack, or to transmit culture through a conservative project, what is it for? Can it be just for itself? The point argued here is that the prime focus of education is the life of the individual, involving an exposure to cultural norms, trends, and aspirations, as all curriculum is, arguably, a selection from culture. It also involves an exploration of present-day problems without looking nostalgically to the known past, or optimistically or pessimistically to an unknown future. Rather, it embodies a rationale that sees educated and capable individuals, who possess strong social orientations and skills, as the best hope for democratically evolving solutions to both known and unknown problems, including the meanings of both democratically and evolving in this context.

We are arguing here a case for liberty as a cornerstone value. We have suggested already that the notion of liberty, as approximated to in liberal democracies may seem too western a concept to have much currency elsewhere. Parekh has argued that this is the case for much of the developing world, and that liberal democracy as a form of government should not be regarded as universalisable. Vincent also argues that the values and practices implicit within liberal justice theory constitute key environmental dangers, although Thomas sees what he calls environmental liberalism within higher education as an essential step towards ecological sustainability.

Enslin rejects Parekh's analysis, firstly, through an historical case that pre-colonial societies in Africa enjoyed traditions of free expression, deliberation, opposition, representation, participation, and checks and balances; secondly on the pragmatic grounds that the newly emerging South Africa has chosen a liberal democratic route; and thirdly, on the more principled criteria that the transcendental qualities of liberalism bring benefits that no other system can, through its emphasis on independent and critical thought and through this, on the development of autonomy and responsibility. Enslin says that the ultimate argument for liberalism is that for societies, and, by implication, individuals within them, to be free to choose right actions, they need the conditions of choice which liberalism seeks to establish. The sustainable development education literature tends not to make this case for liberty and choice, even from within fundamentally liberal democratic societies.

Exploring Necessary Opportunities

These arguments support calls for choice within sustainable development education, for schools and teachers to be free to mediate government policy and educate people about sustainable development free of a priori certainties about outcomes, and unfettered by instructions about what and how to teach. An education which considers issues relating to sustainable development will touch on many issues faced by learners and their families on a daily basis. It is, of course, not always clear what appropriate actions are, and yet actions have to be taken because lives have to be led. Doing nothing is not an option, just as schools' ignoring sustainable development will prove an unsustainable response.

So what can education do in relation to this, and what are practical ways forward? Perhaps educators have four kinds of responsibility: one, to help learners understand why the idea of sustainable development ought to be of interest to them; two, to help learners gain plural perspectives on issues from a range of cultural stances; three, to provide opportunities for an active consideration of issues through appropriate pedagogies which, for example, might begin from learners' and teachers' different interests, helping pupils understand what they are learning and its significance; and four, to encourage pupils to continue to think about what to do, individually and socially, and to keep their own and other people's options open. Doing less than this seems neglectful; doing much more runs the risk of indoctrination. Government agencies and NGOs walk a tightrope when they attempt guidance in such matters because of their need to stimulate without prescribing, and our need to see conceptual frameworks as scaffolding to build learning around, rather than as barriers to new ideas and creativity.

The role of schools is integral to processes of thinking and learning about what might constitute appropriate futures, but its role must be limited, in this case to helping future citizens now, and as their lives evolve. Jensen and Schnack explore such limits when they write:

> ... it is not and cannot be the task of the school to solve the political problems of society. Its task is not to improve the world with the help of pupils' activities. These activities must be evaluated on the basis of their educational value and according to educational criteria. ... The crucial factor must be what students learn from participating in such activities ...

Such a consideration of interests seems necessary to an effective engagement with issues raised by sustainable development, and it offers some protection against forces which would shape society in particular fashions or according to pre-determined nostrums, in ways corrosive of democracy and liberty. Institutions such as schools need to exercise the responsibility that society requires of them, and be free to take up and explore with learners what sustainable development might be in ways that make contingent and contextual sense. Following Enslin, for societies, and for freely cooperating individuals within them, to be free to choose right actions, they themselves need to embody the frames of mind and conditions of choice that enable this. If schools are to be nurseries for such choice and learning, they need encouragement and help in freely experimenting with learning.

CHAPTER 36 OF AGENDA 21 "PROMOTING EDUCATION, PUBLIC AWARENESS AND TRAINING"

In 1992, more than 100 heads of state met in Rio de Janeiro, Brazil, for the United Nations Conference on Environment and Development (UNCED). The so called "Earth Summit" was convened to address urgent problems of environmental protection and socio-economic development. The assembled leaders adopted Agenda 21, a 300-page plan for achieving sustainable development in the 21st century. It called primarily for the adoption of strategies, policies and plans on sustainable development at the national level to be supported by international, regional, sub-regional and non-governmental organizations and also for mobilization of the public at large.

Chapter 36 of Agenda 21 entitled, "Promoting Education, Public Awareness and Training", provides an umbrella for all action related to education for sustainable development, including those foreseen by other UN conferences. In addressing three programme areas,

Chapter 36 encompasses all streams of education, both formal and non-formal, basic education and all the key issues related to educating for sustainable human development, including environmental education.

— Reorienting Education Towards Sustainable Development

— Increasing Public Awareness Towards Sustainable Development

— Promoting Training Towards Sustainable Development

— Reorienting Education Towards Sustainable Development.

Basis for action

Education, including formal education, public awareness and training should be recognized as a process by which human beings and societies can reach their fullest potential. Education is critical for promoting sustainable development and improving the capacity of the people to address environment and development issues. While basic education provides the underpinning for any environmental and development education, the latter needs to be incorporated as an essential part of learning.

Both formal and non-formal education are indispensable to changing people's attitudes so that they have the capacity to assess and address their sustainable development concerns. It is also critical for achieving environmental and ethical awareness, values and attitudes, skills and behaviour consistent with sustainable development and for effective public participation in decision-making.

To be effective, environment and development education should deal with the dynamics of both the physical/biological socio-economic environment as well as human (which may include spiritual) development. These should be integrated in all disciplines, and should employ formal and non-formal methods as well as effective means of communication.

Objectives

Recognizing that countries and regional and international organizations will develop their own priorities and schedules for implementation in accordance with their needs, policies and programmes, the following activities are proposed:

— To endorse the recommendations arising from the World Conference on Education for All: Meeting Basic Learning Needs 2/ and to strive to ensure universal access to basic education, and to achieve primary education for at least 80 per cent of girls and 80 per cent of boys of primary school age through formal schooling or non-formal education and to reduce the adult illiteracy rate to at least half of its 1990 level. Efforts should focus on reducing the high illiteracy levels and redressing the lack of basic education among women and should bring their literacy levels into line with those of men.

— To achieve sustainable development awareness in all sectors of society on a world-wide scale as soon as possible.

— Strive to achieve the accessibility of sustainable development education, from primary school age through adulthood to all groups of people.

— To promote integration of environment and development concepts, including demography, in all educational programmes, in particular the analysis of the causes of major environment and development issues in a local context, drawing on the best available scientific evidence and other appropriate sources of knowledge, and giving special emphasis to the further training of decision makers at all levels.

Activities

Recognizing that countries and regional and international organizations will develop their own priorities and schedules for implementation in accordance with their needs, policies and programmes, the following activities are proposed:

- All countries are encouraged to endorse the recommendations of the Jomtien Conference and strive to ensure its Framework for Action. This would encompass the preparation of national strategies and actions for meeting basic learning needs, universalizing access and promoting equity, broadening the means and scope of education, developing a supporting policy context, mobilizing resources and strengthening international cooperation to redress existing economic, social and gender disparities which interfere with these aims. Non-governmental organizations can make an important contribution in designing and implementing educational programmes and should be recognized.
- Governments should strive to update or prepare strategies aimed at integrating environment and development as a cross-cutting issue into education at all levels within the next three years. This should be done in cooperation with all sectors of society. The strategies should set out policies and activities, and identify needs, cost, means and schedules for their implementation, evaluation and review. A thorough review of curricula should be undertaken to ensure a multidisciplinary approach, with environment and development issues and their socio-cultural and demographic aspects and linkages. Due respect should be given to community-defined needs and diverse knowledge systems, including science, cultural and social sensitivities.

— Countries are encouraged to set up national advisory environmental education coordinating bodies or round tables representative of various environmental, developmental, educational, gender and other interests, including non-governmental organizations, to encourage partnerships, help mobilize resources, and provide a source of information and focal point for international ties. These bodies would help mobilize and facilitate different population groups and communities to assess their own needs and to develop the necessary skills to create and implement their own environment and development initiatives.

— Educational authorities, with the appropriate assistance from community groups or non-governmental organizations, are recommended to assist or set up pre-service and in-service training programmes for all teachers, administrators, and educational planners, as well as non-formal educators in all sectors, addressing the nature and methods of environmental and development education and making use of relevant experience of non-governmental organizations.

— Relevant authorities should ensure that every school is assisted in designing environmental activity work plans, with the participation of students and staff. Schools should involve schoolchildren in local and regional studies on environmental health, including safe drinking water, sanitation and food and ecosystems and in relevant activities, linking these studies with services and research in national parks, wildlife reserves, ecological heritage sites etc.

— Educational authorities should promote proven educational methods and the development of innovative teaching methods for educational settings. They should also recognize appropriate traditional education systems in local communities. Within two years the United Nations system should undertake a comprehensive review of its educational programmes, encompassing training and public awareness, to reassess priorities and reallocate resources.

— The UNESCO/UNEP International Environmental Education Programme should, in cooperation with the appropriate bodies of the United Nations system, Governments, non-governmental organizations and others, establish a programme within two years to integrate the decisions of the Conference into the existing United Nations framework adapted to the needs of educators at different levels and circumstances. Regional organizations and national authorities should be encouraged to elaborate similar parallel programmes and opportunities by conducting an analysis of how to mobilize different sectors of the population in order to assess and address their environmental and development education needs. There is a need to strengthen, within five years, information exchange by enhancing technologies and capacities necessary to promote environment and development education and public awareness.

— Countries should cooperate with each other and with the various social sectors and population groups to prepare educational tools that include regional environment and development issues and initiatives, using learning materials and resources suited to their own requirements.

— Countries could support university and other tertiary activities and networks for environmental and development education. Cross-disciplinary courses could be made available to all students. Existing regional networks and activities and national university actions which promote research and common teaching approaches on sustainable development should be built upon, and new partnerships and bridges created with the business and other independent sectors, as well as with all countries for technology, know-how, and knowledge exchange.

— Countries, assisted by international organizations, non-governmental organizations and other sectors, could strengthen or establish national or regional centres of excellence in interdisciplinary research and education in environmental and developmental sciences, law and the management of specific environmental problems. Such centres could be universities or existing networks in each country or region, promoting cooperative research and information sharing and dissemination. At the global level these functions should be performed by appropriate institutions.

— Countries should facilitate and promote non-formal education activities at the local, regional and national levels by cooperating with and supporting the efforts of non-formal educators and other community-based organizations. The appropriate bodies of the United Nations system in cooperation with non-governmental organizations should encourage the development of an international network for the achievement of global educational aims. At the national and local levels, public and scholastic forums should discuss environmental and development issues, and suggest sustainable alternatives to policy makers.

— Educational authorities, with appropriate assistance of non-governmental organizations, including women's and indigenous peoples' organizations, should promote all kinds of adult education programmes for continuing education in environment and development, basing activities around elementary/secondary schools and local problems.

— These authorities and industry should encourage business, industrial and agricultural schools to include such topics in their curricula. The corporate sector could include sustainable development in their education and training programmes. Programmes at a post-graduate level should include specific courses aiming at the further training of decision makers.

- Governments and educational authorities should foster opportunities for women in non-traditional fields and eliminate gender stereotyping in curricula. This could be done by improving enrolment opportunities, including females in advanced programmes as students and instructors, reforming entrance and teacher staffing policies and providing incentives for establishing child-care facilities, as appropriate. Priority should be given to education of young females and to programmes promoting literacy among women.

— Governments should affirm the rights of indigenous peoples, by legislation if necessary, to use their experience and understanding of sustainable development to play a part in education and training.

— The United Nations could maintain a monitoring and evaluative role regarding decisions of the United Nations Conference on Environment and Development on education and awareness, through the relevant United Nations agencies. With Governments and non-governmental organizations, as appropriate, it should present and disseminate decisions in a variety of forms, and should ensure the continuous implementation and review of the educational implications of Conference decisions, in particular through relevant events and conferences.

Increasing Public Awareness Towards Sustainable Development

Basis for Action

There is still a considerable lack of awareness of the interrelated nature of all human activities and the environment, due to inaccurate or insufficient information. Developing countries in particular lack relevant technologies and expertise. There is a need to increase public sensitivity to environment and development problems and involvement in their solutions and to foster a sense of personal environmental responsibility, as well as greater motivation and commitment towards sustainable development.

Objective

The objective is to promote broad public awareness as an

essential part of global education effort to strengthen attitudes, values and actions which are compatible with sustainable development. It is important to stress the principle of devolving authority, accountability and resources to the most appropriate level, with preference given to local responsibility and control over awareness-building activities.

Activities

Recognizing that countries, regional and international organizations will develop their own priorities and schedules for implementation in accordance with their needs, policies and programmes, the following activities are proposed:

— Countries should strengthen existing advisory bodies or establish new ones for public environment and development information, and should coordinate activities with, among others, the United Nations, non-governmental organizations and important media. They should encourage public participation in discussions of environmental policies and assessments. Governments should also facilitate and support national to local networking of information through existing networks.

— The United Nations system should improve its outreach in the course of a review of its education and public awareness activities to promote greater involvement and coordination of all parts of the system, especially its information bodies and regional and country operations. Systematic surveys of the impact of awareness programmes should be conducted, recognizing the needs and contributions of specific community groups.

— Countries and regional organizations should be encouraged, as appropriate, to provide public environmental and development information services for raising the awareness of all groups, the private sector and particularly decision makers.

— Countries should stimulate educational establishments in all sectors, especially the tertiary sector, to contribute more to awareness building. Educational materials of all kinds and for all audiences should be based on the best available scientific information, including the natural, behavioural and social sciences, and taking into account aesthetic and ethical dimensions.

— Countries and the United Nations system should promote a cooperative relationship with the media, popular theatre groups, and entertainment and advertising industries by initiating discussions to mobilize their experience in shaping public behaviour and consumption patterns and making wide use of their methods. Such cooperation would also increase the active public participation in the debate on the environment. UNICEF should make child-oriented material available to media as an educational tool, ensuring close cooperation between the out-of-school public information sector and the school curriculum, for the primary level. UNESCO, UNEP and universities should enrich pre-service curricula for journalists on environment and development topics.

— Countries, in cooperation with the scientific community, should establish ways of employing modern communication technologies for effective public outreach. National and local educational authorities and relevant United Nations agencies should expand, as appropriate, the use of audio-visual methods, especially in rural areas in mobile units, by producing television and radio programmes for developing countries, involving local participation, employing interactive multimedia methods and integrating advanced methods with folk media.

— Countries should promote, environmentally sound leisure and tourism activities, building on The Hague Declaration of Tourism and the current programmes of the World Tourism Organization and UNEP, making suitable use of museums, herage sites, zoos, botanical gardens, national parks, and other protected areas.

— Countries should encourage non-governmental organizations to increase their involvement in environmental and development problems, through joint awareness initiatives and improved interchange with other constituencies in society.

— Countries and the United Nations system should increase their interaction with and include, indigenous people in the management, planning and development of their local environment, and should promote dissemination of traditional and socially learned knowledge through means based on local customs, especially in rural areas, integrating these efforts with the electronic media, whenever appropriate.

— UNESCO, UNICEF, UNDP and non-governmental organizations should develop support programmes to involve young people and children in environment and development issues, such as children's and youth hearings, and building on decisions of the World Summit for Children.

— Countries, the United Nations and non-governmental organizations should encourage mobilization of both men and women in awareness campaigns, stressing the role of the family in environmental activities, women's contribution to transmission of knowledge and social values and the development of human resources.

— Public awareness should be heightened regarding the impact of violence in society.

Promoting Training Towards Sustainable Development

Basis for action

Training is one of the most important tools to develop human resources and facilitate the transition to a more sustainable world. It should have a job-specific focus, aimed at filling gaps in knowledge and skill that would help individuals find employment and be involved in environmental and development work. At the same time, training programmes should promote a greater awareness of environment and development issues as a two-way learning process.

Objectives

The following objectives are proposed:

— To establish or strengthen vocational training programmes that meet the needs of environment and development and ensure access to training opportunities, regardless of social status, age, gender, race or religion.

— To promote a flexible and adaptable workforce of various ages equipped to meet growing environment and development problems and changes arising from the transition to a sustainable society.

— To strengthen national capacities, particularly in science education and training, to enable Governments, employers and workers to meet their sustainable development objectives as well as to facilitate the transfer and assimilation of new environmentally sound, socially acceptable and appropriate technology and know-how.

— To ensure that environmental and human ecological considerations are integrated at all managerial levels and in all functional management areas, such as marketing, production and finance.

Activities

Countries, with the support of the United Nations system, should identify workforce-training needs and assess measures to be taken to meet those needs. A review of progress in this area could be undertaken by the United Nations system in 1995.

National professional associations are encouraged to develop and review their codes of ethics and conduct to strengthen environmental connections and commitment. The training and personal development components of programmes sponsored by professional bodies should ensure incorporation of skills and information on the implementation of sustainable development at all points of policy- and decision-making.

Countries and educational institutions should integrate sustainable developmental issues into existing training curricula and promote the exchange of their methodologies and evaluations.

Countries should encourage all sectors of society, such as industry, universities, government officials and employees, non-governmental organizations and community organizations, to include an environmental management component in all relevant training activities, with emphasis on meeting immediate skill requirements through short-term formal and in-plant vocational and management training. Environmental management training capacities should be strengthened, and specialized "training of trainers" programmes should be established to support training at the national and enterprise levels. New training approaches for existing environmentally sound practices should be developed that create employment opportunities and make maximum use of local resource-based methods.

Countries should strengthen or establish practical training programmes for graduates from vocational schools, high schools and universities, in all countries, to enable them to meet labour market requirements and to achieve sustainable livelihoods. Training and retraining programmes should be established to meet structural adjustments which have an impact on employment and skill qualifications.

Governments are encouraged to consult with marginalized people, whether geographically, culturally or socially, to ascertain their needs for training to enable them to contribute fully to developing sustainable work practices and lifestyles.

Governments, industry, trade unions, and consumers should promote an understanding of the interrelationship between good environment and good business practices.

Countries should develop services of locally trained and recruited environmental technicians able to provide local people and communities, particularly in deprived urban and rural areas, with the services they require, starting from primary environmental care.

Countries should enhance the ability to gain access to, analyse and effectively use information and knowledge available on environment and development. Existing or established special training programmes should be strengthened to support information needs of special groups.

The impact of these programmes on productivity, health, safety and employment should be evaluated. National and regional environmental labour-market information systems should be developed that would supply, on a continuing basis, data on environmental job and training opportunities. Environment and development training resource-guides should be prepared and updated, with information on training programmes, curricula, methodologies and evaluation results at the local, national, regional and international levels.

Aid agencies should strengthen the training component in all development projects, emphasizing a multidisciplinary approach, promoting awareness and providing the necessary skills for transition to a sustainable society. The environmental management guidelines of UNDP for operational activities of the United Nations system may contribute to this end.

Existing networks of employers' and workers' organizations, industry associations and non-governmental organizations should facilitate the exchange of experience concerning training and awareness programmes.

Governments, in cooperation with relevant international organizations, should develop and implement strategies to deal with national, regional and local environmental threats and emergencies, emphasizing urgent practical training and awareness programmes for increasing public preparedness.

The United Nations system, as appropriate, should extend its training programmes, particularly its environmental training and support activities for employers' and workers' organizations.

EDUCATION FOR SUSTAINABLE DEVELOPMENT

What is 'sustainable development'?

There are some 300 definitions of sustainable development. The most commonly quoted is from Gro Harlem Bruntland, former Prime Minister of Norway, now Director General of the World Health Organisation:

> "development which meets the needs of the past without compromising the ability of future generations to meet their needs".

The 1992 Earth Summit in Rio recognized that the protection of natural environments and human development are part and parcel of each other, therefore 'sustainable development' has a wider remit than environmental concerns. It also embraces social and economic questions such as interdependence, social justice, cultural diversity and equity.

At the Rio Summit, the role of education in promoting sustainable development was made explicit by Agenda 21, the global action plan for the 21st century:

> "Education ... should be recognised as a process by which human beings and societies can reach their fullest potential. Education is critical for promoting sustainable development and improving the capacity of the people to address the environment and development issues".

Agenda 21, 1992.

> Agenda 21 was signed by 178 countries in Rio. Progress will be reviewed at Earth Summit II (or 'Rio +10'), in Johannesburg, August/September 2002.

What is 'Education for Sustainable Development'?

In assessing ways to re-orientate UK education policy to embrace sustainable development, 'education for sustainable development'

> "enables people to develop the knowledge, values and skills to participate in decisions about the way we do things, individually and collectively, locally and globally, that will improve the quality of life now without damaging the planet of the future".

UK Panel for Education for Sustainable Development, 1998.

The key word is education for sustainable development, as opposed to education about sustainable development, a more information-driven concept. In contrast, 'education for sustainable development', like 'citizenship', is a holistic approach for a school's management and the curriculum, not a separate subject. With a clear overlap with the 'citizenship' curriculum, it requires reflection on what to teach, and how to teach in order to:

— clarify and extend the ability of students to think for themselves

— encourages students to reflect and debate issues to enable them to form their own opinions

— foster learning that emerges from discovery and is relevant to the learner's life experience

Action is another key component of 'education for sustainable development' to help young people understand that the responsibility for sustainable development lies with 'me and us' as much as 'them', whoever they are. Therefore, 'education for sustainable development' encourages young people to take action on what they have learned rather than simply absorbing information for regurgitation in exams:

> "The creativity, ideals and courage of the youth of the world should be mobilized to forge a global partnership in order to achieve sustainable development and ensure a better future for all".

Principle 21, Agenda 21, 1992.

Environmental education is a learning process that increases people's knowledge and awareness about the environment and associated challenges, develops the necessary skills and expertise to address the challenges, and fosters attitudes, motivations, and commitments to make informed decisions and take responsible action.

Environmental education enhances critical thinking, problem-solving, and effective decision-making skills, and teaches individuals to weigh various sides of an environmental issue to make informed and responsible decisions. Environmental education does not advocate a particular viewpoint or course of action. The components of environmental education are:

— Awareness and sensitivity to the environment and environmental challenges

— Knowledge and understanding of the environment and environmental challenges

— Attitudes of concern for the environment and motivation to improve or maintain environmental quality

— Skills to identify and help resolve environmental challenges

— Participation in activities that lead to the resolution of environmental challenges

Why environmental education is important

Environmental education improves our everyday lives by:

— Protecting Human Health

— Advancing Quality Education

— Creating Jobs in the Environmental Field

— Promoting Environmental Protection Along with Economic Development

— Encouraging Stewardship of Natural Rèsources

Protecting human health

The link between environmental challenges and human health is a major cause of public concern about the environment. Lead poisoning from paint and pipes, air pollution, pesticides in water and food supplies, increased threats of skin cancer from depletion of the ozone layer, and other environmental and health issues are of growing concern to Americans, especially effects on children and future generations. Environmental education can help prevent or mitigate environmental human health problems by providing the public with information on the causes of environmental pollution, how pollutants may affect health, how to assess real versus exaggerated risks, and how to make informed and responsible decisions that prevent or mitigate the effects of pollution on health.

Advancing quality education

Educators and public officials generally believe that improvements are needed in the nation's public education system to enhance student learning. Many educational scholars and practitioners agree that students are not doing well at thinking, reasoning, analyzing, or problem-solving.

Many goals of education reform emphasize the need to strengthen core subjects such as math, science, and geography;

teach across subject areas; improve critical-thinking and problem-solving skills; and relate learning in the classroom to the needs and issues of the community. Environmental education has a tremendous potential to contribute to these goals of education reform. For example, it can strengthen teaching in many core subjects, especially science, because science is the basis for solving many of our environmental challenges.

At the same time, environmental education can promote interdisciplinary teaching because environmental topics can be addressed from many different perspectives, including scientific, historical, and cultural. Environmental education can also bring local environmental challenges into the classroom to improve analysis and problem-solving skills.

Creating jobs in the environmental field

Protecting the environment creates new jobs for Americans. Employment opportunities in the environmental field cover the spectrum of careers from manual labor to high technology and management. For example, there is an increasing demand for individuals with specialized scientific and technical skills to develop more effective pollution prevention and control technologies in areas such as air pollution control, environmental energy sources, hazardous waste management, resource recovery, and instrument manufacturing. Environmental education and training can help ensure an adequate supply of well-trained environmental personnel to deal with the nation's increasingly complex environmental challenges.

Environmental education's emphasis on criticalthinking and problem-solving skills equip learners in dealing with rapidly changing technologies in the workplace. Environmental education also opens new economic opportunities as the U.S. exports environmental skills and technologies to other nations.

Promoting environmental protection along with economic development

Our future depends on the ability to use the Earth's resources sustainably. The United Nations World Commission on Environment and Development defines sustainable development as "meeting the needs of the present without compromising the ability of future generations to meet their own needs."

Sustainable development poses two fundamental education challenges. One is to promote informed decisions that are conducive to sustainability. The other is to teach the benefits of integrating conservation with the need for economic development. Environmental education contributes to sustainable development efforts by demonstrating ways to promote informed decisionmaking and teach the benefits of linking conservation and economic development. Environmental education research has identified key strategies for developing education programs that lead to responsible decisionmaking, and practitioners have developed program models for incorporating a range of perspectives into the resolution of issues. These educational tools and strategies can be applied to efforts to ensure sustainable development.

Encouraging stewardship of natural resources

Interest in protecting America's natural resources, including species and their habitats, arises from the respect most Americans hold for our nation's past and a belief in its future. This interest also stems from a strong desire to protect and enjoy nature and to pass it on to our children. There is a need to increase understanding that the health of individual species can be strong indicators of the health of the entire environment and that biological diversity has ecological and economic importance. Environmental education enhances the public's understanding of the need for healthy plant and animal life and biodiversity. It also educates the public about how their actions affect natural ecosystems and how positive steps taken to minimize impacts on these ecosystems will translate into improvements in our overall environment.

OUTDOOR EDUCATION AND ENVIRONMENTAL RESPONSIBILITY

Outdoor education offers programs that provide opportunities for students to become environmentally conscious citizens. However, awareness of environmental issues is not enough to preserve our world of limited natural resources. Students must also be prepared to recognize their environmental responsibilities and act upon them. This involves behaving in ways that sustain and nurture the natural environment and consider the needs of others. Such a sense of environmental responsibility is a potential outcome of outdoor education under certain conditions.

In the past, outdoor educators conducted studies to assess the effect of environmental outdoor education programs on knowledge and attitudinal change. The knowledge-attitude-behavior change model described by Matthews and Riley holds that an increase in knowledge will lead to a change in attitude which will in turn influence behavior. Consequently, environmental knowledge and attitudes have been frequently evaluated when attempting to determine the effect of outdoor education programs on the development of environmental responsibility.

For example, Bryant and Hungerford conducted a study in which they presented an instructional unit on environmental problems to kindergarten students. They then asked the students to describe their own and others' responsibilities as a way of measuring the students' verbal commitment to action. The researchers found that students appeared more environmentally conscientious at the conclusion of the environmental education unit. They concluded that kindergarten children could understand environmental issues and citizenship responsibilities.

In another study, Jaus assessed the short- and long-term impacts of environmental instruction on the attitudes of third graders. Driver and Johnson studied the long-term benefits of the Youth Conservation Corps program, which combines outdoor work opportunities and environmental education for youth ages 15 to 18. The youths indicated that they had become more environmentally aware as a result of the program. Finally, Shepard and Speelman measured the impact of participating in an outdoor education program at resident 4-H camps in Ohio on children ages 9 to 14.

Although the experimental treatment did not develop significantly more positive environmental attitudes, researchers found that program length had an effect on positive environmental attitude development. This has led outdoor educators to look to related fields for techniques that have successfully created positive behavioral change in students. Matthews and Riley conclude that the following have not worked in bringing about ethical, behavioral change in students: "lectures, excessive moralizing, external(ly) derived codes of ethics/conduct, adults setting the ethics agenda, and teachers/leaders as authoritarian figures". As a result, outdoor educators have directed more attention to environmental action activities that develop responsible environmental behavior.

For example, Ford and Blanchard state that outdoor activities can create an initial sensitivity toward the environment, the first and essential step on the path toward increased understanding of environmental processes, increased understanding of our place in, and dependence upon, the ecosystem, and...to action on behalf of the environment.

Matthews and Riley seem to support Ford and Blanchard's assertion that environmental responsibility is best developed outdoors. Involvement in outdoor activities stimulates interest in the outdoors, which in turn motivates students to learn about the natural environment. Other studies seem to support this position. Ramsey and Hungerford studied the effects of an outdoor education curriculum package that used environmental issue investigation and action training on 7th-grade students.

Howe and Disinger also concluded that outdoor experiences made a significant impact on student attitudes and found that outdoor settings were effective in teaching awareness of environmental issues. In addition, they reported that the most effective instructional strategies for developing environmental responsibility were case studies, field trips, community inventory projects, and community action projects. Other effective methods include small group discussions, dilemma discussions, role playing, the use of role models and mentoring, participation in community clubs, and peer teaching.

Matthews and Riley found that the programs most likely to change behavior involve concrete, environmentally positive, action-oriented experiences; a relevant context; and long-term involvement, support, follow-up, and reinforcement by role models. Hungerford and Volk add that effective programs allow students to gather in-depth knowledge; require students to use critical thinking skills; and involve application of what students have learned.

In Just Beyond the Classroom, Knapp proposes that effective outdoor education programs focus on the community, involve service learning, be interdisciplinary, use problem-based learning methods, allow for cooperation, and include time for reflection. Attarian seems to support these recommendations when he states,

...developing values is a lifelong process. As educators we can provide our students with the experiences and tools to help them become more knowledgeable about the environment and their place in it. Participation in outdoor pursuits classes and programs can give all of us the opportunity for challenge, adventure and excitement. Perhaps most of all, the outdoor experience offers to a chance to explore and shape our values, attitudes, and behaviors towards the environment and ourselves.

ENVIRONMENTAL EDUCATION—KNOWLEDGE TO BEHAVIOR CHANGES

Goals and objectives of many state and local environmental education programs have included developing students with knowledge, skills, positive attitudes and motivation to take action, to prevent and to resolve environmental problems. Individuals who exhibit responsible environmental behavior on a broad range of problems have:

(1) Knowledge of relevant environmental concepts;

(2) Knowledge of environmental problems and issues;

(3) Concern for the quality of the environment;

(4) Knowledge of action strategies that may be used for resolving an issue;

(5) Belief that their action can make a difference.

(6) Commitment to take action; and

(7) Experience in action based activities.

Data indicate that a good knowledge of environmental concepts is not sufficient; knowledge of environmental issues, issue skill analysis, and attitudes and values related to taking action are also necessary for the individual to take action and to act responsibly. Some states, such as Wisconsin, have developed state curriculum guides that recognize the need to provide for these variables in school programs, beginning early in the school program and continuing the emphasis throughout the school program.

The Wisconsin program supports a hierarchical approach and that (1) concepts, attitudes and skills develop over time, (2) effective programs involve both cognitive and affective emphases, (3) effective programs require issue analysis, and (4) experiences should be provided that help the individual develop the feeling that their efforts and actions can make a difference with real issues and problems.

Environmental curriculum developers have been working to develop and test materials to help students to exhibit more responsible environmental behavior.

ENVIRONMENTAL APPROACHES MAKE RESPONSIBILE ENVIRONMENTAL BEHAVIOUR

Conservation for Children

Conservation for Children is a program for use in grades 1-6 designed to increase (1) conservation awareness, (2) understanding of basic scientific environmental, and conservation concepts, and (3) conservation action. The program includes a variety of basic skill activities in the areas of language arts, mathematics, social studies and science with conservation concepts and conservation action. The infusion approach used in the program provides a conservation emphasis throughout the curriculum. The program also provides a continuing emphasis on conservation concepts and behaviors over time by providing materials for six years.

Materials can be used to replace or to supplement current materials so relatively little additional class time is needed. Six grade-level curriculum guides and one all-level guide (activities, resources) are available. Data indicate most pupils who use the materials on a regular basis learn over 80 percent of the concepts and implement conservation practices at home.

Environmental Issues and Actions

Hungerford and his associates have analyzed research on variables related to the development and demonstration of environmentally responsible behavior and have designed and tested a set of instructional materials based on this research. The materials stress a hierarchical-approach involving four levels of activities.

1. Ecological Concepts: This goal level attempts to provide the learner with the ecological knowledge that will permit him/her to make ecologically sound decisions with respect to environmental issues. This knowledge would include (but not be limited to) such concepts as individuals and populations, interaction, limiting factors, biogeochemical cycling, abiotic influences, homeostasis, succession, etc.

2. Conceptual Awareness: This goal level attempts to develop a conceptual awareness (i.e., knowledge) of how individual and collective behaviors influence the relationship between quality of life and the quality of the environment, as well as how human behaviors result in issues which must be resolved through investigation, evaluation, decision-making, and citizenship action.

3. Issue Investigation and Evaluation: This goal level attempts to develop the knowledge and skills needed to permit learners to investigate environmental issues and evaluate alternative solutions for remediating these issues. It also provides opportunities for students to actually investigate and evaluate issues.

4. Environmental Action Skills: Training and Application: This goal level attempts to develop those skills needed for learners to take positive environmental action for the purpose of resolving or helping resolve environmentally-related issues.It also involves the development of action plans by the students and provides them with the opportunity to implement those plans if they desire.

Research data indicates that behavior change usually will not occur if students are exposed only to Goals 1 and 2. The data also indicates that behavior will change if students are thoroughly exposed to Goals 3 and 4 in addition to 1 and 2. The quality of the students environmental actions also tends to improve when they have used issue analysis and investigation. The materials Hungerford and his associates have developed include six modules: (1) Environmental Problem Solving; (2) Issue Investigation (Basics); (3) How to Gather Information; (4)

Interpreting Data; (5) Investigation of Issues; and (6) Environmental Action Strategies.

Studies report that effective use of the modules has usually required about 18 weeks of instruction and activities, but alternative approaches have been suggested in the literature. The modules have been tested primarily at the middle school and junior high school level, but could probably be adapted to grade levels as low as four and certainly could be used with older students in secondary schools and postsecondary institutions.

PROMOTING ENVIRONMENTAL EDUCATION

A general tenet of environmental education is that humans use ecosystems, affect ecosystems, are affected by ecosystems, exist in complex interactions with ecosystems, and are ultimately accountable for their effects on ecosystems. Many environmental educators postulate three ways of viewing this interaction: dominion, humans over nature; stewardship, humans caring for nature; and union, humans as part of nature.

Environmental education is a process of moving individuals toward stewardship and ultimately a union view of the relationship of people with nature. Environmental education is process more than it is content: environmental education is usually infused into various curricula, particularly in the sciences and is an integration of disciplines with no exclusion of strategies and with synthesis of information that can occur more readily than when disciplines are isolated. In this process, cognitive understanding is not sufficient; affective and behavioral development is necessary to affect significant value, belief, behavioral, and cognitive shifts in individuals. When such shifts do occur, environmental education is no longer a "band-aid" but is an agent of transformation enabling epistemological change.

How such shifts are achieved is fully dependent upon the learner, the teacher, and the setting. Yet, there are general precepts that can guide a teacher to fully incorporate a philosophy of environmental stewardship or union into all teaching settings. One is that a holistic, experiential, and value-neutral presentation of the content enhancing creativity is achieved through the emotional, intellectual, and ethical development of the individual. Another suggests that understanding the complexities of the interrelationships with the environment is a necessary condition to the maintenance and improvement of environmental quality. Given demands on the educator, whether in a formal or a non-formal setting, environmental lessons, experiences, and activities must be integrated into the curriculum and limited instructional time.

Integration must deal equally with all environmental concern areas, and not focus on a narrow topic at hand. It is possible to examine the means by which these precepts are incorporated into teaching by considering three philosophical positions. The first can be called "imposition"; the second "infusion"; and the third, "framing." As the label implies, imposition is placing onto the required study a subject called "environment" or a specific focus within the environment. Libraries and teachers' shelves are full of materials created for specific topics such as water quality, solid waste, energy, rainforests, acid rain, ad infinitum.

Whether a special curricular guide, a course of study, or a special study segment, these materials are often the most readily available to educators and the most simply introduced into the teaching/learning setting. Such resources are often funded by or developed by industry, specific issue-focused groups, government agencies, or environmental groups, all of which have a desire to get information into the classroom. The quality and value of the materials are as wide ranging as the topics; yet in the hands of a master educator, even lesser quality guidelines can provide a strong basis for learning that will shape present and future environmental decisions. Unfortunately, many of these materials address topics in isolation and deny the "complex nature of the natural and built environments resulting from interactions of physical, biological, social, economical, and cultural aspects".

When treated in this manner, environmental education suffers because it is undefinable in terms of how it relates to existing programs. Infusion involves incorporating environmental concerns into existing curricula and content. For the educator, the challenge is how to permeate learning experiences with environmental education. In many cases, infusion may be thematic for a class or group, but often involves creating opportunities to include environmental issues as the application of the field of study (e.g., math, physics, biology). Myriad resources provide educators with quick references for activities that incorporate environmental themes or topics into traditional disciplinary approaches. Some widely used resources are "Clearing" and "Ranger Rick"; in addition, numerous collections of activities for environmental education are available for the educator.

Philosophically, the infusion approach attempts to integrate or infuse into the mainstream of public schooling the knowledge, skills, attitudes, experience, and commitment that will result in informed decisions, responsible behavior, and constructive actions. Environmental education, therefore, includes science, math, social studies, language arts, health, and physical education. Environmental education is the grounding for all schooling and the foundation for organizing schooling into natural systems rather than by arbitrary disciplinary boundaries.

Disinger and Howe suggest that infusion often "flounders on the reticence of discipline-oriented curriculum designers and teachers" to rely on content from other than their own area of expertise. The third philosophic approach suggests that the arbitrary boundaries of traditional disciplines be eliminated in lieu of creating a framework of study in which subject areas become related and integrated rather than isolated and disparate. This break with tradition can be best accomplished when educators and students investigate, interpret, explore, manage, discover, and make decisions about larger encompassing studies (Indiana DOEd). This approach frames learning in a manner that challenges old assumptions about teaching and learning.

Hines et. al. identified four factors that comprise environmental education:

(a) knowledge of environmental issues;

(b) knowledge of specific action strategies to apply to the issues;

(c) the ability to take action on environmental issues; and

(d) the ownership of certain affective qualities and personality attributes.

Using these factors as a basis for constructing learning, disciplines become less distinct as life skills are developed, and the application of traditional disciplinary skills drives the need to know of the learner. The result is not only an acquisition of traditional knowledge cognitively, affectively, and behaviorally, but also an ability to transfer such learnings.

Framing learning for environmental education requires moving beyond traditional methods of classroom teaching. Science-Technology-Society schools and concept/magnet schools are approaches that embrace such change through using traditional disciplinary skills to define technological, scientific, and societal aspects of real world problems that use problem-solving and decision-making processes to address the problems. A less radical approach is to use supplementary curricular guides that, at least for a few learning segments, transform the learning process into an environmental focus rather than a discipline-based and separated structure.

Just as with environmental issues themselves, there is no uniformity on how to best introduce and use environmental issues in the teaching and learning exchange. Each individual can champion the manner that is consistent with personal beliefs about learning and teaching. Forcing a teacher to incorporate fundamental principles of environmental education through a means that is not comfortable to the individual is like trying to make the environment fit into all disciplines.

NEW APPROACHES TO TEACHING ENVIRONMENT AND HEALTH

Population growth, intensive industrialization, food processing, transport systems and the modern way of life all significantly contribute to the deterioration of the environment. Pollution affects all basic physical elements of the environment: air, water and soil, upon which human health depends. Therefore it is crucial that the efforts taken to protect the environment become more extensive, organized and coordinated.

This process is well underway in developed regions, and interest in solving environmental problems is increasing in developing areas. Numerous programs have been introduced to stimulate efficient prevention of environmental pollution in both regions and across national and regional borders. Such extensive support has also lead to the rapid development of the concept of environmental health. Environmental health is a multidisciplinary area, which requires collaboration by many professions including medicine, biology, chemistry, technology, sociology and psychology among others. Knowledge of environmental problems is key - it is of the utmost importance for all these experts. However, the issue is not only identification of an environmental problem, but also expertise to enable the collaboration of experts from different sciences to research various aspects of the same problem and to take action to lessen or prevent further environmental pollution. Even for these experts developing interactive cooperation on a common project is a most difficult task.

The COPERNICUS Programme, sponsored by the Association of European Universities (CRE) aims to incorporate environmental health into all relevant university curricula and to help develop teaching materials which will prove valuable to teachers and students alike. As a result, a textbook called Basic Environmental Health was written in collaboration with the World Health Organisation (WHO), United Nations Environment Programme (UNEP) and UNESCO. The book, scheduled to be completed in the fall, is intended for teachers, students and experts from different sciences who work on environmental problems. WHO, UNEP, and UNESCO also organized a seminar on Environment and Health in April 1996 in Budapest, Hungary. The course was intended for university teachers and others active in environmental health teaching with an objective to evaluate the new teaching kit. Twenty-three scientists from the Danube Basin took part in the course which was held at the National Institute of Public Health. The participants represented various professions - doctors, biologists, chemists and a mathematician - all of whom in one way or the other work in environmental health teaching. The course was guided by the authors of the book, the scientists of WHO and the most outstanding Hungarian experts on environmental issues.

The main objectives of the course were as follows:

— to promote Environmental Health teaching

— to increase the knowledge of environmental sciences

— to strengthen teaching skills, including the ability to use a variety of interactive teaching methods and problem-based exercises

— to promote the incorporation of local environmental health problems into teaching contexts

— to encourage the participants to share their work and teaching experiences.

Students of environmental health differ greatly according to their basic profession, interests and previous knowledge. Well-organized and extensive knowledge can surpass the local influence and professional diversity, both of which hinder reaching creative solutions. The process of studying environmental health should not only include assembling information and knowledge about a particular problem but should also encourage students to use innovative and interactive teaching methods efficiently.

INDEX